The Engineer's Contribution to Contemporary Architecture

G000067085

To Tim with my Best Regards

Tony

Series editors

Angus Macdonald
Remo Pedreschi

Department of Architecture
University of Edinburgh

To Tim with my Best Regards

Terry

The Engineer's Contribution to Contemporary Architecture

ANTHONY HUNT

Angus Macdonald

Thomas Telford

Endorsed by

RIBA Publications

Published by Thomas Telford Publishing, Thomas Telford Ltd, 1 Heron Quay, London E14 4JD.
URL: http://www.thomastelford.com

Distributors for Thomas Telford books are
USA: ASCE Press, 1801 Alexander Bell Drive, Reston, VA 20191-4400, USA
Japan: Maruzen Co. Ltd, Book Department, 3–10 Nihonbashi 2-chome, Chuo-ku, Tokyo 103
Australia: DA Books and Journals, 648 Whitehorse Road, Mitcham 3132, Victoria

First published 2000

Also available from Thomas Telford Books

The Engineer's Contribution to Contemporary Architecture – Eladio Dieste. R. Pedreschi ISBN 0 7277 2772 9
The Engineer's Contribution to Contemporary Architecture – Heinz Isler. J. Chilton ISBN 0 7277 2878 4
The Engineer's Contribution to Contemporary Architecture – Peter Rice. A. Brown ISBN 0 7277 2770 2

The Architecture of Bridge Design. D. Bennett ISBN 0 7277 2529 7
An Introduction to Cable Roof Structures. Second edition. H. A. Buchholdt ISBN 0 7277 2624 2

A catalogue record for this book is available from the British Library

ISBN: 0 7277 2769 9

Designed by Acrobat
Printed and bound in Great Britain by The Cromwell Press, Trowbridge, Wiltshire

Acknowledgements

I would like to thank all those who have assisted me in the making of this book. Special thanks are due to Norman Foster, Nicholas Grimshaw, Richard Rogers and John Young for granting me interviews. I am also grateful to colleagues and friends for advice with the typescript, especially André Brown, John Chilton, Alice Crossland, Remo Pedreschi and Iain Boyd Whyte. Thanks are also due to: the staff at Anthony Hunt Associates; Foster and Partners; Nicholas Grimshaw and Partners, especially Donnathea Campbell; and Richard Rogers and Partners, for help with picture research; the staff of Anthony Hunt Associates who made visits to their office useful and enjoyable; and to the editorial and production staff at Thomas Telford Ltd, especially to Nick Lowndes, James Murphy and Elaine Stott.

I am especially grateful to Diana and Tony Hunt for their hospitality and for their help and advice with the typescript and design, and to Tony for making the time available to discuss his many interesting projects with me in detail.

Finally, I should like to thank my wife Pat for her support and encouragement throughout, for her expert help with matters of book-making and for many useful conversations which we had concerning the issues discussed in this book.

Angus J Macdonald

Edinburgh

September 2000

Preface

A book which deals with the work of Tony Hunt and his office, Anthony Hunt Associates (AHA), might be thought to be principally about engineering. This book is mainly concerned, however, with the contribution which Tony Hunt made to the development of British architecture in the second half of the twentieth century. For nearly 40 years AHA has been producing structural engineering that is celebrated for its visual quality and its technical elegance. The firm has worked, and continues to work, with most leading British architects, on a considerable number of seminal buildings and has been the recipient of numerous architectural awards.

Perhaps its greatest achievement, however, has been the part that it has played in redefining the relationship between architects and engineers. For most of the twentieth century the role of the structural engineer, in the context of architecture, was that of the person who worked out how to build a form that was devised by someone else. The rare exceptions to this were engineers who worked *as* architects rather than *with* architects, for example, the early masters of reinforced concrete vaulting, such as Eugène Freyssinet, or architect/engineers such as Felix Candela, Pier Luigi Nervi and Eduardo Torroja.

Tony Hunt, the founder of AHA, has continually challenged the traditional role of the engineer, preferring to work instead with architects, as part of a design team, from the very beginning of a design when the concept is formulated and throughout the entire design and construction process. His particular abilities and his interest in the visual aspects of design have allowed him to form fruitful collaborations with architects and to contribute significantly to the development of particular forms of Modern architecture. Among them is the style which came to be known as High Tech, in which exposed structure of refined appearance played a major visual role. Other, more recent developments include complex structurally-exciting buildings of organic or landform shapes. The purpose of this book is to explore the nature of these collaborations.

This is not therefore a comprehensive account of the work of AHA or of Tony Hunt. Rather it is an exploration of the nature and significance of the relationships that Tony Hunt has been able to establish with leading architects. It deals with his contribution to the development of specific strands of Modern architecture and to the re-establishment of the engineer as an active participant in the creation of architectural form. For this reason the book concentrates on Hunt's work with four of Britain's most prominent architects, namely Norman Foster, Richard Rogers, Michael Hopkins and Nicholas Grimshaw, and is concerned principally with work carried out in the 1960s, 70s and 80s – the period in which the particular style associated with these architects was first realised in built form.

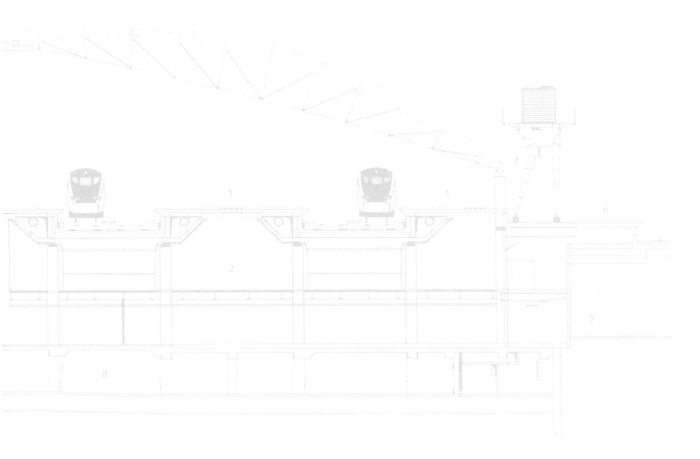

Contents

Chapter One

Architecture and engineering in Britain
in the second half of the twentieth century

Chapter One
Architecture and engineering in Britain in the second half of the twentieth century

Tony Hunt is a structural engineer who made a significant contribution to the visual and technical aspects of late twentieth-century architecture and who continues to influence current practice, both personally and in terms of the philosophy of teamwork which is central to the operation of his office. He is someone who sees his role as being 'in at the beginning'. This quotation formed the title of a section which he contributed to a book on the early work of Norman Foster[1] in which he described his experiences working with both Foster and Richard Rogers at the very beginning of their careers. It is, however, relevant to many other aspects of his working life, which now spans over 50 years; for nearly 40 of these he has been the principal partner in his own practice. In Tony Hunt's words 'I have been around for a hell of a long time'.[2] Throughout that time he has been involved with many 'beginnings' and this book will attempt to review these and assess their importance to British architecture.

When Tony Hunt set up his practice in the early 1960s, international Modernism dominated new building throughout the world, especially in Europe and in the USA. The situation in Britain had its roots in the fairly lively architectural scene which had existed there in the period immediately before the 1939–45 war when Modern architecture had made its first appearance and in which émigrés from continental Europe and from the British Dominions had played a significant part. Britain was, at that time, one of

the few major European countries in which the government was not actively discouraging the production of Modern architecture in favour of some version of a nationalist style. It is not surprising, therefore, that it should have attracted some of the most forward-looking architects of the time.

Individuals such as Walter Gropius, Erich Mendelsohn, Berthold Lubetkin and Serge Chermayeff brought the most advanced Modern architectural ideas to Britain in the 1930s and, together with a small number of local practitioners such as Maxwell Fry and Conell, Ward and Lucas, produced some excellent examples of the white, rectilinear architecture that characterised the heroic phase of early Modernism. The Canadian, Wells Coates, was also active in Britain at this time and founded the MARS (Modern Architectural Research) group, the British wing of the Congres Internationaux d'Architecture Moderne (CIAM), in 1932.

An interesting aspect of this strand of architecture in Britain during the pre-1939 period was the contribution which was made to it by structural engineers. The most significant of these was Owen Williams who was an architect/engineer and who produced a remarkable breadth of work ranging from reinforced-concrete bridges to large-scale buildings. He is best known for his architecture, however, most particularly the Boots Factory in Nottingham (*Fig. 1.1*), on which he acted as architect and engineer, and the Daily Express

building in London, which was carried out with the architects Ellis and Clarke. Williams' importance can perhaps be judged from the following quotation

'... the scope of English architecture between the wars would have been much reduced had it not been for [Williams'] remarkable large-scale works and above all for the extraordinary reinforced-concrete Boots Pharmaceutical Factory[3]'.

Williams was the first engineer in Britain to establish close relationships with architects in the Modern period. Two continental engineers, Ove Arup (a Dane) and Felix Samuely (an Austrian) were also active in London at this time and worked with the architects of the MARS Group on several of the significant early Modern British buildings. Arup's work with Tecton in the Highpoint flats in London and with Samuely and Tecton in the design of the Penguin Pool at London Zoo (*Fig. 1.2*) are examples. Samuely's collaboration with Mendelsohn and Chermayeff, which produced the De La Warr Pavilion at Bexhill-on-Sea, was another.

All of these are examples of collaborations between engineers and architects in which engineers were concerned with architectural as well as technical aspects of design. Thus, within the very active group of Modern architects centred on MARS, a tradition of close collaboration between architects and engineers began to emerge in Britain. It is possible to see here the beginning of the type of working relationships that produced High Tech in the

Fig. 1.1. Boots Pharmaceutical Factory, Beeston, England. Owen Williams, 1932.

Fig. 1.2. Penguin Pool, London Zoo, London, England, 1933. Berthold Lubetkin and Tecton with Ove Arup and Felix Samuely.

1960s and 1970s. All of the leading engineers of High Tech can be linked to the practitioners of the 1930s. Tony Hunt may be regarded as a pupil of Samuely. Peter Rice and Ted Happold each worked with Ove Arup.

After the war of 1939–45 the architectural climate changed in Britain; the exiles from continental Europe, who had created the architectural excitement of the 1930s, had mostly either left or ceased to practice but the time seemed to have come for the ideas of Modernism to be accepted by the British architectural establishment which, in the 1930s, had largely eschewed Modernism and been content to produce architecture in historicist styles of one kind or another. This change in the architectural climate coincided with the need for a great deal of new building, associated with the post-war reconstruction of cities and with the setting-up of the Welfare State. Modernism dominated the building programmes of British governments of all political hues during the 1940s, 50s and 60s: educational and health-care buildings by the hundred and houses and flats by the thousand were designed and constructed in the spirit of pre-war Modernist theories of architecture and urban planning.

By the 1960s, international Modernism had fragmented into a number of sub-styles. Perhaps the least evident of these in Britain was the minimalist architecture of metal and glass, based on strictly rectilinear forms, which had been developed in the USA by architects such as

Ludwig Mies van der Rohe and the firm of Skidmore, Owings and Merrill. The Lake Shore Drive Apartments in Chicago (1949–51), the Seagram Building in New York (1955–58) (*Fig. 1.3*), the IIT Campus in Chicago (1939–56) and Lever House in New York (1951–52) had all been recently completed and gave aesthetic expression to the precision and refinement that could be achieved using the products of industry. These buildings belonged to the mainstream of rationalist Modernism and were, in a sense, functionalist, because by providing spaces that were functionally neutral, they represented a recognition that, in the Modern world, spaces within buildings were likely to be subject to a variety of uses. Although not well represented in Britain, this version of Modernism affected the work of Tony Hunt because it exerted a strong influence on the architects with whom he collaborated.

In Britain in the 1960s a mini 'battle of the styles' was in the process of being resolved. The older generation of British architects, who had finally espoused Modernism after the war, continued to resist its most austere forms and favoured the Romantic Modernism of the buildings and pavilions of the Festival of Britain (1951) which was typified by the one permanent surviving monument of the exhibition, the Royal Festival Hall (1951) (*Fig. 1.4*). This was a softened version of the severe 'white' 1930s Modernism of Gropius, Mendelsohn and Lubetkin. It was a Modern architecture tempered by the British tradition of the Picturesque and the anti-Modern Arts and Crafts

Movement and 'the British love of the whimsical'.[+]

The younger generation of British architects reacted against this diluted Modernism and favoured a grittier version which came to be known as New Brutalism and reinstated, with stylistic differences, the puritanical austerity of the early masters. It had various roots, perhaps the strongest being the sophisticated primitivism of the late work of Le Corbusier in buildings like the Unité d'Habitation in Marseilles (1948–52). The genre first came to Britain in the secondary school at Hunstanton (1952–54), by Alison and Peter Smithson. In theory, New Brutalism was concerned with truth and objectivity: truth in the sense that buildings should reveal their functions, constituent materials and method of construction; objectivity in the sense that the ego of the architect should be suppressed and forms derived which were expressive of their function.

By the late 1950s and early 1960s Brutalism had spread to the USA, notable examples being Louis Kahn's Richards Medical Research Centre, University of Pennsylvania, Philadelphia (1957–61) and the City Hall, Boston, Massachusetts by Gerhard Kellmann, Knowell McKinnell and Edward Knowles (designed 1961). A formalist kind of Brutalism, which shared with European Brutalism the idea of being faithful to materials, but in which forms were determined from considerations of aesthetics rather than from function, also developed in the USA, in the work of architects such as Eero Saarinen and Philip

Johnson. This, in turn, recrossed the Atlantic and appeared in Britain in the work of firms such as Powell and Moya, Chamberlain, Powell and Bon, and Stirling and Gowan (*Fig. 1.5*).

The strand of Modern architecture that was closely linked to engineering, and which had appeared in Britain in the 1930s with Williams, Arup and Samuely, continued into the 1950s and 1960s. The firm of Ove Arup and Partners was the most significant in this period and the Rubber Factory at Brynmawr, Wales, is perhaps the best example (*Fig. 1.6*). Buildings like this fitted well into the Brutalist genre.

Brutalism was the principal influence on new building in Britain in the early 1960s and, as the state welfare programmes progressed, the architectural media burgeoned with articles accompanied by well-photographed images describing schools, hospitals, university buildings and mass housing schemes in a vocabulary of exposed concrete and breeze block which were intended to celebrate the ideas of truth and objectivity. It was an age of realism and similar things were happening in other artistic fields. The 'angry young men' of literature and drama, for example, were at the same time swinging British theatre away from the cosy upper-middle class world that it had inhabited in the 1930s into the stark realities of working-class domesticity. The buildings of New Brutalism were of their time, in that they were the architectural equivalents of the 'kitchen sink drama'.

Then and since, critics and architectural

Fig. 1.3. Seagram Building, New York, USA. Ludwig Mies van der Rohe, 1958.

Fig. 1.4. Royal Festival Hall, London, England. Leslie Martin and others, 1951.

influential Modern buildings world-wide'.[7] The architects and their apologists were confident of the ability of Modern architecture to transform the world through design.

This was the architectural world into which Tony Hunt's practice was born. Brutalism reigned supreme in Britain and exemplified many of the key features of Modern architecture: it was international, abstract, and anti-historicist. In the early post-war years, when the political mood favoured reform on the socialist model, it also retained its link with morality — the idea of using architecture as a vehicle for transforming society for the better.

This mood remained influential through the 1960s, during which time Hunt was establishing his relationship with Foster and Rogers in Team 4. This was the period which saw the completion of two of their significant collaborations, the Creek Vean House and the Reliance Controls building, both of which conform in some measure to the ideas of Brutalism. In each case the architects adhered to the idea of 'truth to materials'; all of the building elements were visible and there was no applied ornamentation. At Reliance Controls there was also a social agenda: the even-handed treatment of workers and management was entirely consistent with the social aspects of the Modernist agenda.

The Team 4 buildings also had features that were original. They were of more refined appearance — literally much less brutal — than the mainstream Brutalist buildings. This was a

journalists have made extravagant claims for such architecture. Large-scale housing developments such as the Roehampton Estate in London (1952–55) by Hubert Bennett, Leslie Martin and Robert Matthew of the London County Council were described as 'probably the finest low-cost housing in the world'.[5] The school at Hunstanton by Alison and Peter Smithson was 'the young Smithsons' stroke of genius'[6] and the Leicester Engineering Building by James Stirling and James Gowan (1963) was called 'one of the most

Fig. 1.5. Engineering Building, Leicester University, Leicester, England. James Stirling, 1963.

consequence of the design process used to produce them, in which Foster and Rogers worked closely with Hunt to push the capabilities of the materials to their limits in the pursuit of slender, elegant forms. In this respect the group was abandoning the formalism of Mies at the Farnsworth House and the Smithsons at Hunstanton, where the dimensions of the steelwork were determined from visual considerations rather than from technical criteria. At Reliance Controls the element sizes were pared down to the minimum required for adequate strength and rigidity. It was an approach that allowed the building to evolve essentially from functional considerations tempered by firm guidance from the collective aesthetic senses of its creators. The Reliance Controls building also introduced a new visual vocabulary to Brutalism in the form of the aesthetic of the 'found' industrially-made component. The Team 4 buildings were, nevertheless, based on the same set of architectural ideas that informed Brutalism and, considered in this light, High Tech, which was initiated at Reliance Controls, may be seen as largely an extension of Brutalist ideas.

It is interesting, however, that the aspects of the Reliance Controls building which were new — the all-welded exposed steel frame and the finely detailed cladding system — were the parts of the design with which Tony Hunt, the engineer member of the group, was most closely involved. The drawings in his hand of the details of the steel frame and of its relationship to the cladding testify to this (Fig. 3.10) and draw attention to the importance of his role in the creation of this building which revolutionised the treatment of industrialised architecture in Britain.

There seems little doubt that the arrival of Foster and Rogers on the British architectural scene, and the development of their association with Hunt, were significant events. Most of their contemporaries looked to the 'masters' for

17

inspiration — most especially Mies van der Rohe, Le Corbusier and Alvar Aalto. But Foster and Rogers were trying to do something new and different. In Rogers' words

'By our generation we had already had 30 or 40 years of that [i.e. following the 'masters'] and I suppose we were looking for a different approach — the idea that you could actually build buildings out of a kit of parts (weld on site) and put the cladding up in an informal way without having worked it out in a proportional way. This is a workshop approach rather than the Modern classicism of Mies. We were trying in some ways not to achieve the formalism of Mies.'[8]

Foster and Rogers were, of course, also influenced by the 'masters' but they had in

addition been exposed to the architecture of the West Coast of America, that strand of Modernism which was concerned with making architecture out of the products of industry, in particular the Case Study Houses of Craig Ellwood. They were also excited by the British engineering tradition, and most especially by the spectacular enclosures erected by the nineteenth-century engineers. This interest in technology coupled with a desire to do something different and the fortunate meeting with Hunt began something new in British architecture which became a strong movement in the last three decades of the twentieth century and which was responsible for some of the most important British buildings of the period. The movement also developed an international dimension with buildings such as the Centre Pompidou in Paris and the Hong Kong and Shanghai Bank headquarters in Hong Kong.

By the early 1970s, when Foster, Hunt and Rogers were becoming established with this particular version of Brutalism, the climate of architectural opinion was changing. Within ten years of the completion of Reliance Controls, the supremacy of international Modernism and, in Britain, of Brutalism and of its successor High Tech, was challenged firstly by the Postmodernists[9] and then by Deconstruction.

The debate concerning which approach to architecture was valid in the late twentieth century and beyond has continued ever since and has taken place against a background of widespread public disaffection with the

Fig. 1.6. Brynmawr Rubber Factory, Brynmawr, Wales. Architects Co-Partnership with Ove Arup and Partners.

Photo: Architectural Review

international Modernism of the 1950s and 60s, much of which failed, catastrophically, to live up to its early promise. 'Architects were the *bêtes noires* of the 1960s, associated by the public with unsympathetic high-rise housing, insensitive office developments and bunker-like art galleries.'[10] The architectural establishment, including the largely apologist architectural press, mounted a vociferous defence and became increasingly distanced from the opinions of the public at large. By the late 1970s and through the 1980s, however, Postmodernism and Deconstruction dominated the insulated world of the architectural media as the architecture that was considered critically interesting.

The existence of this debate raises the question of whether architectural Modernism should be regarded as a movement which should now make way for other approaches to design or be regarded as an approach which is still relevant and innovative and which has retained its vigour. It will be the job of future historians to provide the answer to this question. Current opinion is divided, and there are convincing arguments on both sides although considerable confusion results from the different semantic conventions used by the various participants.

Much of the debate has been conducted in the language of rhetoric. The account by Diane Ghirardo is scholarly and detached but is fairly dismissive of the achievements of late Modernism. In a book that claimed to 'examine the architectural world of the last quarter-century'[11] relatively little space is devoted to late Modernism. British High Tech, which has produced some of its most exciting visual images, many of them engineered by Hunt, rated a mere four out of 240 pages and was not mentioned in the section on industrial buildings — a building type to which it has contributed a great deal. Of the 'well-serviced shed' she has this to say:

'Even when it is realised with skill and sensitivity, the limitations of the multipurpose shed are obvious: endless repetition of the same motif, producing

Fig. 1.7. Vitra Design Museum, Basel, Switzerland. Frank Gehry, 1989.

Photo: E & F McLachlan

environments that may well be clear and calm, but are of mind-numbing and irritating sameness.[12]

So much for the Sainsbury Centre. And of the Centre Pompidou, one of the most spectacular of late-Modern buildings, Ghirardo states:

'Rarely has so much uninteresting information been communicated on a façade with such chromatic aggressiveness.'[13]

The advocates of Postmodernism in the 1970s and 80s would have shared these views[14] but Ghirardo is not much more sympathetic to the Postmodern and Deconstruction architects. She argues that there never has been a truly post-Modern architecture and that the so-called Postmodern and Deconstruction architectures were simply variations of the Modern. Of the Postmodernists, she says:

'… the fundamental continuity between Modernist and post Modernist (sic) architects derives from the reassertion of the power of form, and hence the primacy of design to the exclusion of other strategies for improving cities and living conditions.'[15]

Of Deconstruction, she says:

'… in their [Deconstruction architects'] absolute indifference to issues of context, their exaltation of the role of the architect as form giver and interpreter of society, it is difficult to discern significant departures from dogmatic Modernism except in the particularities of form.'[16]

If these arguments are accepted — and others have made similar observations[17] — the conclusion would necessarily be that, in an age of post-Modern consciousness, architecture has

remained, in essence, firmly Modern. In other words, architectural Postmodernism and Deconstruction are not fundamentally different from Modernism because they share with it too much that is inappropriate in the post-Modern world. The Postmodern and Deconstruction architects seem therefore to have continued to operate within the paradigm of Modernism in the broad sense at least.

The fact that Postmodernism and Deconstruction have occupied increasing amounts of space in the architectural media of the last 20 years may therefore have given a misleading impression of their significance. The reality may be that, as some of the Modernists had done before them, the Postmodern and Deconstruction architects borrowed philosophy from other fields and made nothing more out of it than a style. The chaotic forms of Deconstruction (*Fig. 1.7*), for example, may appear to reflect contemporary thinking in science and philosophy (although some would doubt that they do so in anything but a highly superficial stylistic sense), but may in fact represent simply an imposition on the users of buildings of forms that are impractical because they have been invented solely out of considerations of stylistic fashion (and are, in that sense, part of the Modernist paradigm), rather than being developed from any dialogue with everyone involved. Some would consider that a truly post-Modern form would be the result of a process designed to satisfy the requirements of all

of the people with a stake in the building. Instead, the architects of the Postmodern and Deconstruction buildings have operated, as Ghirardo has pointed out, with all the certainty and lack of dialogue of the straight Modernists.

A similar but different analysis to that of Ghirardo is provided by Gablik[18] who considers that the post-Modern in art practice — she is not concerned with architecture *per se* — may be divided into a *de*-constructive strand (i.e. a critique of Modernism) and a *re*-constructive strand (the later being truly post-Modern in that it moves on beyond critique). What is uncertain is whether Postmodern or Deconstructive architecture are for the most part even seriously engaged in critique or are merely concerned with 'avant-gardeism'.

It can be argued, therefore, that most architecture is still Modern and that what happened in the 1980s and 90s was yet another battle of the styles — all of them either sub-styles or offering superficial stylistic critiques of Modernism. Seen in this light, the late Modernists with whom Tony Hunt has been involved have produced work which could be considered as relevant to the contemporary architectural scene as that of most Postmodernists or Deconstructionists.

The practitioners of late-Modernism continued to innovate and to develop the ideas of Modernism through the 1970s, 80s and 90s. High Tech was an example of this process; it represented a fresh approach in two significant ways. Firstly, it involved a visual vocabulary which was continuously refreshed by the introduction of new technologies. One of the consequences of this was that the design teams actually accomplished many of the goals that were set, but not realised, by the early Modernists. Hunt and his collaborators were, for example, responsible for significant developments in the technology of glass cladding and this found architectural expression in the Willis, Faber and Dumas building (*Fig. 4.22*), which, with its curvilinear all-glass perimeter was a closer realisation of Mies's famous image of the glass-clad office building (*Fig. 1.8*) than anything that Mies himself was able to build.

A second novel aspect, pioneered by those who developed High Tech, was a new way of working — the design team made up of equal partners from different disciplines — which was a discursive forum in which architects, engineers and others evolved a design together so that visible structure was created which worked in both aesthetic and technical terms. It required the abandonment of the idea of the autonomous 'master'. The transition has a truly post-Modern dimension because design by teamwork and consensus, which has always been the ethos of Tony Hunt's practice, belongs to the post-Modern world in which the emphasis moves from top down hierarchical structures to the networks and feedback loops of systems thinking. This aspect of the work of Tony Hunt and his office is fundamental; it is not a stylistic overlay as is the

case with many of the buildings that belong to the Postmodernist and Deconstruction schools.

The most recent architecture with which Hunt's office has been involved continues to be radically innovative and relevant. The train shed at Waterloo Station, for example, by Hunt and Grimshaw (*Fig. 7.6*), may appear to be simply a twentieth-century version of the nineteenth-century iron and glass railway station, with recent technical innovations such as weldable cast steel joints. It may also appear to be High Tech. In fact, the steelwork possesses a level of complexity which could not have been accomplished before the age of computer-aided design and which is suggestive of the complexity of a living organism, one of the appropriate metaphors for the philosophies of the emerging organicist paradigm. Although, therefore, this building may be seen as a development of High Tech it is so significantly distinct as to merit a different name, perhaps Organi-Tech. The same could be said of the Eden Project (*Figs 2.20* and *2.21*), also with Grimshaw, and of the dome at the National Botanic Garden of Wales (*Figs 2.18* and *2.19*), with Foster and Partners. The realisation of the complex organic or 'landform'[19] shapes of these buildings gives appropriate visual expression to the sophistication of contemporary technology. They also provide intimations in several senses of what might be involved in a re-constructive post-Modern architectural practice even while they remain linked to the Modernist agenda concerned with the celebration of technological progress.

Fig. 1.8. Glass skyscraper project, Ludwig Mies van der Rohe, 1922.

Chapter Two
Tony Hunt and Anthony Hunt Associates

Chapter Two
Tony Hunt and Anthony Hunt Associates

Introduction

The structural engineering technologies which were developed in the twentieth century, particularly those associated with the 'new' materials of reinforced concrete and steel, exerted a profound influence on the evolution of Modern architecture. The extent of this influence grew as the century progressed and occurred in parallel with changes which took place in the relationships between architects and engineers. In Britain, in the 1960s and 70s, a small group of architects and engineers working in the tradition of Arup, Samuely and Williams, revolutionised the visual treatment of exposed structure and this led to the evolution of a distinct strand of Modernism that came to be known as High Tech. Tony Hunt was a key figure in its creation and this book is concerned largely with the story of the birth and development of that movement.

So far as structural design is concerned, the movement was dominated by the work of three engineering practice: Ove Arup and Partners, Buro Happold and Anthony Hunt Associates. The last of these was and is still by far the smallest[20] but it has, nevertheless, been responsible for the engineering of some of the most important buildings to be built in Britain in the late twentieth century, including the Reliance Controls factory at Swindon (1966) (arguably the first British High Tech building) (*Fig. 2.1*); the Willis, Faber and Dumas building in Ipswich (1975) (a totally innovative version of the multi-storey office

building) (*Fig. 4.22*); the Sainsbury Centre for the Visual Arts in Norwich (1978) (perhaps the most pristine of all 'decorated' sheds) (*Fig. 4.13*), and the International Rail Terminal at Waterloo Station in London (1992) (the first train shed of note to be built in Britain since the great nineteenth-century structures of Brunel, Wyatt and Barlow).

The contribution made by Anthony Hunt Associates (AHA) to the development of late Modern architecture in Britain has therefore been disproportionate to the size of the practice. It makes work which is highly imaginative, supremely competent and which is always carried out with a light touch. The ethos of the firm has been very much determined by the personality of its founder and current principal director, Tony Hunt. It has a number of aspects.

Firstly, there is a passion for the making of structures that are elegant from a purely technical viewpoint. A structure by AHA makes appropriate and efficient use of material and will often be found to contain devices, such as hinge joints placed so that they redistribute internal forces in clever ways, which make them intellectually satisfying. Technical performance is never compromised in order to satisfy non-structural requirements or agendas. If a proposed form is problematic from a structural viewpoint, AHA either finds a way of dealing with it that is satisfactory structurally or persuades the other members of the design team that a different form would be more appropriate.

Secondly, there is a concern for appearance,

a desire to make structures which are beautiful as well as practical. This aspect of the firm's ethos, which is crucial to its relationship with architects, also stems from Tony Hunt, who is greatly interested in all aspects of visual design from buildings to furniture to graphic design and typography. He is also committed to the idea that the well-designed, exposed structure has a significant contribution to make to the development of architectural vocabularies which celebrate the ideas of Modernism. He has worked with architects with similar objectives and similar levels of commitment to this idea, and this fortunate coming together of individuals contributed significantly to the development of a new kind of relationship between architects and engineers in the second half of the twentieth century.

Thirdly, although the firm is small, the work of AHA is eclectic, encompassing a very wide range of project types from civil engineering, through all kinds of building structures, to small-scale works such as exhibition pavilions. It makes use of all of the conventional structural materials and some that are not so conventional. (There is currently, for example, a design for a 20 m-span footbridge made entirely of glass.)

The firm is prepared to tackle virtually any project and Tony Hunt maintains that he has never turned down an invitation to become involved in a competition entry. This has caused him to be accused, by the 'stiffer' element of the engineering profession, of dilettantism, a view which might

Fig. 2.1. The Reliance Controls factory, at Swindon, England, was the first High Tech building and introduced to Britain a new architectural vocabulary for small industrial buildings. Team 4, 1966.

Photo: Anthony Hunt Associates

have some validity if there were a shred of evidence to suggest that the range of activity of the firm was causing a dilution of design standards, which there is not.

Fourthly, there is informality. Tony Hunt is himself a friendly and outgoing person with an informal manner and this sets the tone of the practice. There is no standing on ceremony at AHA, just proper communication between individuals. People find that if they have something interesting to say or good ideas to communicate they will be listened to. Young engineers are given the opportunity to develop their ideas and to see them realised in built work. This congenial atmosphere must have been a factor in the success of the firm and important in relationships with architects and clients. People are attracted to work which can be enjoyed on a human level and this has certainly been the case at AHA.

An important aspect of the working methodology adopted at AHA is the emphasis which is placed on teamwork. Each project is allocated a dedicated design team but the collaborative process extends beyond the confines of a particular design team. At key stages in the development of a project design critiques are held in which the ideas involved are exposed to other design teams in the office whose members contribute comments and ideas. Teamwork therefore operates at more than one level with the whole office potentially being involved with a design.

Tony Hunt has therefore set up a practice that produces engineering of a very high quality. He has also made a place in which young engineers can operate in a spirit of fun and commitment and which clients and collaborators find congenial. It is a unique combination which has produced a unique body of work.

Tony Hunt and Anthony Hunt Associates

Tony Hunt was born in London in 1932. From an early age he was interested in making things that had complex technical agendas. He was fascinated by model aircraft, for example, and even successfully designed one himself 'from scratch.'[21] Aeroplanes are complex artefacts, and flyable model aeroplanes, because they must be stable flying systems that self-rectify when disturbed, are among the most sophisticated and underestimated of mechanical devices. Tony Hunt's interest and success in making flyable model aeroplanes was an early indication that he possessed the combination of feel and knowledge that would make him a very successful engineer. He also confesses to having been interested in that other schoolboy favourite of the mid-twentieth century, the Meccano set. This was a toy consisting of a kit of reusable metal parts that provided opportunities for children (and their parents!) to exercise imagination in the creation of miniature machines and structures.[22]

On leaving school, in 1948, Tony Hunt worked initially as a technician in a university laboratory. During this period he studied engineering at night school, firstly for one year at Northampton Polytechnic and then, following a career move into engineering, at the Westminster Technical College, where he passed ONC and HNC exams in 1956. His first job in engineering was as an articled apprentice in a firm of consulting engineers in the City of London. The apprenticeship route to a profession was still an option in the late 1940s and this was fortunate because his parents could not afford to fund him through a university course.

The articled job turned out to be a disappointment. The work was routine and his colleagues and employers uninspiring. Fortunately, however, there was excitement to be found elsewhere in a London which was gradually pulling itself out of the austerity that followed the 1939–45 war. He was a Promenade Concert 'fanatic' and also enjoyed the 100 Club where the latest jazz music was played. The Festival of Britain, for which he became a season ticket holder, was especially significant because it was there that he discovered Modern architecture. He still possesses the copy of the *Architects' Journal* devoted to this exhibition, which was a celebration of British design of all kinds. Tony Hunt's response to the exhibition was to consider changing to architecture as a career because it seemed to offer more exciting challenges than the mundane engineering work with which he was involved on a day-to-day basis. He was persuaded against this by his father — a decision which he says he has never regretted.

Hunt senior's task was perhaps made easier by the fact that Hunt junior's enthusiasm for engineering had been maintained by the spectacular structures that he saw in the Exhibition — particularly the Skylon and the Dome of Discovery. The structural design of the Skylon was carried out by Felix Samuely, the gifted engineer who had first come to prominence as the man who carried out the complex structural analysis of the curved ramps of the Penguin Pool at London Zoo, by Berthold Lubetkin and Ove Arup, which is one of the most graceful pieces of reinforced concrete ever constructed. In the early 1950s, Samuely was the most exciting engineer around in Britain and Tony Hunt wrote to him in 1951 asking for a job. He was interviewed by Frank Newby, of Felix J. Samuely and Partners, was offered a place and worked for the firm for the next eight years.

Frank Newby was a very significant early influence on Hunt. Especially important were the close working relationships that Newby formed with architects which schooled Hunt in the design-by-teamwork methodology that was to be crucial to his success when he set up in practice on his own.

Samuely's office provided the ambience in which a true apprenticeship in architectural engineering might be served. Samuely himself was obsessed with the idea of minimal structure and Tony Hunt found himself working on structures that pushed the capabilities of steel and reinforced concrete to their limits. This was the best possible training for someone who, when he eventually set up in practice on his own, would work with architects who demanded elegant and ever more slender structures in forms and general arrangements which were sometimes far from ideal from a structural point of view. It was the experience gained while working for Samuely that gave Tony Hunt the confidence to produce the very slender, minimalist structural elements of early High Tech, such as the spectacularly thin purlins of the Reliance Controls building (*Fig. 2.2*). He gained a wide range of experience at Samuely's, including steel and reinforced-concrete structures, prestressed-concrete structures, composite structures and folded-plate structures.

Much of the work that Tony Hunt was involved with at Samuely's was carried out with the Lyons Israel Ellis Partnership, a forward-looking and innovative firm of architects that, at the time, employed a number of talented young architects who would subsequently rise to prominence in Britain. Among these were Neave Brown, James Stirling, James Gowan, John Miller and Patrick Hodgkinson. All of these would eventually practice in their own right and be in a position to offer work to engineers. The friendships which Tony Hunt made at this time were to be useful sources of work when he eventually set up in practice on his own. His collaborations with the young architects who worked for Lyons Israel Ellis were also significant in another respect because they gave him direct experience of the design-team working

Photo: Anthony Hunt Associates

Fig. 2.2. Reliance Controls factory under construction. The extreme slenderness of the purlins is evident in this view.

Cantù and received a commendation for his entry. This led him to show the design to Terence Conran, then establishing himself as the individual who would popularise well-designed Modern furniture in Britain, and Conran promptly offered him a job. Tony Hunt left the Samuely office to work for Conran and found himself part of a small design team which included Conran himself, Christina Smith, John Stephenson and John Betmead. He worked on a variety of small-scale design projects including furniture, exhibition stands, partition systems and interiors.

Tony Hunt's real interest, however, was in designing on the scale of buildings and six months later he left Conran to join a small multi-disciplinary architectural practice (Hancock Associates) based in Wallingford, as an Associate Partner. This firm would break up within 18 months but, while it lasted, it provided Hunt with the opportunity to work on a variety of design projects ranging in scale from delicate timber structures to the winning design for Reading Civic Centre. It also gave him further experience of closely-knit multi-disciplinary design teams.

When Hancock Associates dissolved in 1962 Hunt moved back to London and contacted his old friend Frank Newby who advised him to start his own practice. Anthony Hunt Associates was founded on 1 August 1962 and consisted of Hunt himself and one assistant (David Sharples) working from Hunt's home in St Peter's Square in London. Other early associates were Richard

methodology which would be of great subsequent importance.

'...it was through them (LIE) I got used to working closely with architects. This happened very naturally, so I have tended to take that idea of a working relationship very much for granted. It certainly was a great surprise, later, to come across architects who seemed happy to just send you their finished design drawings to 'engineer' up.' [23]

The years with Samuely were therefore crucial to Tony Hunt's development but his free spirit and continual quest for excitement did not fit him for life as a junior employee, in which much of the work is inevitably routine. His design-led roving eye was constantly on the lookout for fresh challenges and in 1959 he entered a furniture design competition run by

Clack, Brian Foster, Laurie Fogg and Leslie Stebbings. Fortunately, with the 1960s building boom getting underway, there was plenty of work. Many young architects were then establishing new practices and some of these had become personal friends of Hunt during his days with Samuely and were able to provide him with work. Hunt also received commissions that were passed on by Frank Newby from the fashionable and therefore overloaded Samuely office and acknowledges that this patronage by Newby provided welcome stability for his practice in the first two years of its existence.

AHA quickly grew into an organisation employing approximately 30 staff. Significant early jobs were a hotel and ice rink on Speyside with Russell, Hodgson and Leigh, a student hall of residence for Leicester University with Castle, Park, Dean and Hook and a block of flats in London with Howard and Rotherham.

These jobs were crucial to the establishment of the firm but, although they were not without interest, they did not present Tony Hunt with the kind of challenge that his experience and abilities had prepared him to meet. In the previous ten years he had worked with some of the most talented and innovative designers then practising in Britain. He was also passionate about the aesthetics of engineering and the influences in this field were the works and writings of Torroja, Waschmann and Eames. This background, together with his interest in architectural design and with visual design generally, fitted him for collaborations with architects who wished to develop new types of architecture based on exposed structure. The opportunity to become involved with this kind of architect came about by chance based on opportunities created by Hunt himself.

From the beginning, Tony Hunt recognised the necessity of providing a congenial working environment for his staff. His firm quickly outgrew the accommodation available in his house and by 1963 it was occupying part of a three-storey building in Covent Garden. Initially, the building was too large for the practice and so parts of it were let to other organisations. Among these was the architect Neave Brown, who had recently set himself up in architectural practice, and whom Hunt had met while working with Samuely. This connection proved to be a very significant one because, according to Tony Hunt, it was at a dinner party at Neave Brown's house that he met Richard and Su Rogers. This resulted in Tony Hunt working with Team 4 and establishing the relationships with Norman Foster and Richard Rogers that were to be so significant in the birth of British High Tech.[24] Team 4 and the subsequent Foster and Rogers offices provided the kind of design environment that Hunt had been looking for, in which small groups of enthusiastic young designers from various disciplines worked collaboratively and discursively to evolve novel architectural forms and vocabularies, particularly those which involved exposed structure.

Chapter Two
Tony Hunt and Anthony Hunt Associates

Photo: Anthony Hunt Associates

Fig. 2.3. Housing development at Alexandra Road, London. The engineering here was competent rather than ground-breaking but the project was, nevertheless, important for the consolidation of Anthony Hunt Associates' position as leading structural engineers. Sidney Cook, Camden Borough Council Architects Department, 1978.

Hunt's work with Team 4 in the 1960s began with small-scale domestic buildings in masonry and reinforced concrete and, while these had novel and interesting forms (see chapter 3), they were not ground-breaking. It was the Reliance Controls building at Swindon, completed in 1966, and the last building designed by Team 4 before the practice broke up in 1967, which would lead to something both exciting and new. The elegant, exposed welded-steel structure, clean lines and crisp detailing of this building represented a new architectural vocabulary for industrial building in Britain and gave birth to a whole new strand of late Modern

architecture. Tony Hunt's contribution to this design, which relied heavily on the visual qualities of an exposed structure that he had largely devised, drew attention to his qualities as an engineer who could combine good engineering with aesthetics.

Neave Brown may perhaps be regarded as the 'godfather' of AHA because, apart from the introduction to Rogers mentioned above, he was also principally responsible for AHA being commissioned for the job which bankrolled the office for most of the 1970s. This was the comprehensive housing redevelopment at Alexandra Road in Swiss Cottage, London for Camden Borough Council (*Fig. 2.3*). This came about because Neave Brown had taken a job with Camden Borough Council after his own embryo practice had run out of work. He joined the local authority's Architecture Department when it was about to embark on what was to be the last major social housing project in London in the twentieth century and which marked the end of an era in which the provision of social housing was a government priority. This scheme became controversial because it outlived the political ideas that constituted its philosophical rationale. (Following the election of Margaret Thatcher's Conservative Government in 1979 the idea of society was temporarily declared invalid in Britain.) The Alexandra Road housing, which was completed in 1978, was, nevertheless, one of the most successful mass-housing projects ever constructed.

The chief architect at Camden in the late 1960s, when the scheme was commissioned, was Sidney Cook. Cook had remained committed to the ideas of early Modernism and, in particular, to the idea that architects, as the designers of decent living places for the urban working population, had a role to play in the establishment of a just society. Hunt, together with Max Fordham as the services engineer, was appointed to the job at the suggestion of Neave Brown, who became the job architect. In Tony Hunt's words, this was 'the job that set me up'.[25] He also comments that it was 'a brave decision' on the part of Sidney Cook to employ such young practitioners and further states that in his opinion 'it would not happen now'. The presence of people who were prepared to take brave decisions may well be the explanation for the success of the project. Everyone who was directly involved — local politician, architect or engineer — was young and deeply committed to its ideals.

The Alexandra Road redevelopment was the largest job that AHA had yet attempted.[26] It consisted of 520 dwellings arranged in five 6-storey terraces, three 4-storey terraces and three blocks of 3-storey houses, all with garage accommodation for each dwelling. In addition to the housing the contract included a community centre, a school for handicapped children, shops, a youth club for the Inner London Education Authority, a public car park, playgrounds, a five-a-side football pitch and an amphitheatre. The superstructure of the housing blocks consisted of

Fig. 2.4. The Newport High School, Gwent, Wales was the winning scheme in an architectural competition in which Anthony Hunt Associates had contributed to six of the entries including one by Foster Associates. Evans and Shalev.

Fig. 2.5. The factory for SAPA (Scendinaviska Aluminium Profiler AB) factory. was a large-scale shed involving a 21 m span portal framework consisting of a horizontally-spanning Warren girder supported on square hollow-section columns. It had a 'smooth' skin of profiled metal cladding and in many respects anticipated the Sainsbury Centre.

exposed reinforced-concrete cross-walls and slabs supported on a grid of columns at ground level. Column-and-beam frames in reinforced concrete were used for the school and community centre.

AHA's work on Alexandra Road was highly competent, but the principal interest of the scheme was not in the engineering, which was appropriate, but in the architecture which, then and since, has provided a focus for debate on social housing issues. In the discussion of the many interesting architectural issues that the project raised, the quality of the engineering went unnoticed. This is often the case, especially in buildings in which spans are short and spectacular structures are not required. Good engineering, in this context, produces very simple and straightforward forms and therefore tends to

be taken for granted. This may be one of the reasons why the recognition that follows from successful architecture tends to be accorded to the architects alone rather than to the engineers as well.

Two other large jobs undertaken by AHA which began in the late 1960s, were Newport High School and the Library at Leicester University. The architects for the Newport School (*Fig. 2.4*) were Evans and Shalev and the commission was the result of a successful competition entry. Hunt had in fact been the engineer for six of the entries to this competition including one by Foster Associates that was to be the prototype for their ground-breaking collaboration over the building for IBM at Cosham (see chapter 3). The structure of the Newport building was a beam-and-column frame in reinforced concrete and, as at Alexandra Road, the engineering was competent rather than exciting and an entirely appropriate response to the problems posed by the design.

The Leicester Library, with Castle, Park, Dean and Hook, was technically a very advanced building based on a combined structure and services arrangement in reinforced concrete. The engineering here was more interesting but the building was fairly conventional in an architectural sense. This project was to prove a rock on which AHA almost foundered. In 1967, when the design was at an advanced stage, the project was suddenly halted due to government cuts in funding for education and Tony Hunt found himself unexpectedly deprived of a large amount of fee income when the staff complement had been built up to cope with the work of three large jobs. Suddenly there was a cash-flow problem and the bank decided to withhold salary payments, leaving AHA on the verge of bankruptcy.

The situation was saved by David Wolton, a personal friend of Tony Hunt, who guaranteed the firm to the bank, or more exactly, and to Tony Hunt's great satisfaction, to a different branch of the same bank to which the account was transferred and where it has remained ever since. David Wolton — a hop merchant and businessman — was married to Georgie Cheeseman, one of two sisters — the other being Wendy — who, with Norman Foster and Richard Rogers, were the co-founders of Team 4. Wendy Cheeseman married Foster and, following the break up of Team 4 in 1967, was the co-founder of Foster Associates.

The episode of the near bankruptcy clearly illustrates the role played by personal relationships in the establishment of the London-based group of architectural and engineering practices which evolved the British High Tech style. A small number of like-minded people used their combined talents and abilities to produce built form which contributed significantly to the history of British architecture. Individually they could not have created the style because each brought to it a particular and individual combination of ability and experience. One important factor was their enjoyment of each other's company. They worked together but also met socially and, occasionally, stayed in each other's houses or took holidays together. Included in this group were Norman and Wendy Foster, Richard and Su Rogers, Neave Brown and Tom Hancock, who taught Hunt to sail.

Although the three largest jobs undertaken by AHA in the late 1960s and early 1970s (Leicester Library, Newport School and the Alexandra Road housing) were all executed in reinforced concrete, Tony Hunt's real interest lay in developing the ideas that had emerged in the Reliance Controls building. The 1970s were important not only for Hunt but also for British architecture because it was in this decade that

Fig. 2.6. Sobell Pavilion for Apes and Monkeys, London Zoo, London, England. An enclosure of steel mesh supported on MERO system space frames. The links between the mesh and the structure were springs to reduce impact effects when the animals jumped onto the mesh. John Toovey, 1973.

Fig. 2.7. Timber dome, Crestone, Colorado, USA. The client specified that the structure should be free of ferrous metal components. Keith Critchlow, 1981.

British High Tech, which may be regarded as having begun with the Reliance Controls building by Team 4 and Hunt, became established. As the movement developed, a number of its most significant British buildings were engineered by Hunt. These were buildings for Computer Technology, IBM, SAPA (*Fig. 2.5*), Willis, Faber and Dumas, and the Sainsbury Centre with Foster Associates (see chapter 4), the Spender and Rogers Houses and the factory for Universal Oil Products with Richard Rogers and Partners (see chapter 5) and the Hopkins House with Michael and Patty Hopkins (see chapter 6).

These High Tech buildings were the flagship projects with which Hunt was involved in this period but other interesting projects were the Sobell Pavilion for Apes and Monkeys at London Zoo with John Toovey, who was architect to the Zoo, a timber-lattice dome in Colorado, USA, with Keith Critchlow, and a series of schools with Hampshire County Architects Department.

The most spectacular part of the Sobell Pavilion (*Fig. 2.6*) was a steel-mesh enclosure supported on a MERO space frame. The MERO structure, which acted as a play frame for the animals, was supported both centrally, on an inverted pyramid of tubes, and at its corners, and also had cable bracing for stability. The mesh that formed the enclosure had coil springs incorporated into it to absorb the energy of the animals jumping onto it, some of which were large, and the panels of mesh were laced together with stainless-steel strands to provide a further spring effect.

At the client's request the timber dome in Colorado (*Fig. 2.7*) was designed to be free of any ferrous metal components. It consisted of a series of interwoven laminated-timber ribs glued on site and clad in timber, formed as a continuous spiral around the dome framework and finished with hand-made clay tiles. The Hampshire schools were built under the enlightened architectural policy devised by the chief architect, Colin Stansfield Smith. Newlands School, which is a pair of linked single-storey buildings with very neatly detailed exposed-timber roof trusses, was Tony Hunt's favourite.

The range of work being carried out through the 1970s was typical of the kind of portfolio that the Hunt practice has held throughout its entire existence. It falls into three categories. Firstly, there were projects that were acknowledged to have made a significant contribution to twentieth century architecture. The Willis, Faber and Dumas building, the Sainsbury Centre for the Visual Arts, the Hopkins House and the Hampshire schools fall into this category. Secondly, there were projects that represented a job well done — the firm operating as a structural engineering consultancy, maintaining high professional standards, and contributing to buildings which provided clients with what they wanted but which are probably not so significant as those in the first category. The Newport School and the Leicester Library are of this type. Thirdly, there were the small projects

Fig. 2.8. The INMOS Microprocessor factory, at Newport, Gwent, Wales. The structure is remarkable for the ingenious site joints, all but one of which involved only a single pin. These greatly facilitated the erection process. The pioneering use of weldable cast steel allowed joints of complex shape to be manufactured economically. Richard Rogers and Partners, 1982.

which were interesting because they invited novel solutions to unusual problems. The Sobell Pavilion and the Colorado Dome are examples.

In 1972, at the beginning of this highly productive decade, AHA had grown to occupy all four floors of another building in Covent Garden and had a staff of four associates, a business manager, eight engineers, 16 designer/detailers and two secretaries. It was carrying out work to a total value of £19 million including factories, offices, schools, universities, a hospital and housing for both private and public sectors. The office was split into four design teams each headed by an associate who was responsible for ensuring that all activities necessary to the completion of jobs were carried out (e.g. surveys, calculations, drawings, legal consents). Tony Hunt

was responsible for the initial design and planning of all projects and kept a watchful eye on the progress of all current work. Weekly meetings were held to discuss job progress and monthly meetings also took place to discuss job costs and future staff requirements. The monthly meetings also provided a forum for a general exchange of information on technical subjects.

In 1976, in the middle of this decade of feverish activity, Tony Hunt took the rather surprising decision to open a second office in the country, near Cirencester in the Cotswold Hills, and to base himself there. The decision was surprising because it took him away from the close-knit community of London-based architects, services engineers and quantity surveyors with whom he was collaborating so successfully. Tony

Chapter Two
Tony Hunt and Anthony Hunt Associates

Hunt himself says that he did this largely because he simply liked the idea of living and working in the country but also because he believed that it might provide opportunities for obtaining work. He had in fact owned a cottage in the Berkshire Downs close to one owned by Foster. During this period he had a great deal of contact with Foster both socially and professionally.

Eleven staff members moved to Cirencester in 1976 and two years later, following a downturn in work, the decision was made to close the London office. The move to Cirencester proved successful, however, and the 1980s began with exciting new projects in the form of the INMOS Microprocessor factory at Newport in Wales, with Richard Rogers and Partners, the Patera lightweight building system with Michael Hopkins and the Schlumberger Research Facility and Testing Station, also with Hopkins.

INMOS (Fig. 2.8) was the first job on which Hunt had collaborated with Rogers for approximately ten years. From his own recollection the circumstances of his appointment were serendipitous. He happened to be in the Rogers office one morning and became involved in a discussion about the project with a group of people, including the client Ian Barron, with whom Hunt had previously worked on the Computer Technology building with Foster Associates in the mid 1970s. Hunt ended up being appointed as engineering consultant on the INMOS project and he regards this as one of the most exciting jobs that he has ever done.

Hunt's idea for the structure, described in detail in chapter 4, was that it should be 'pure, totally pin-jointed, diagonally-braced only where necessary — and exoskeletal'.[27] The structural design was carried out by Hunt and Mike Davies working so closely with a small design team from the Rogers office that, in Hunt's words, they would not now 'be able to determine quite who designed what'.[28] The INMOS factory, with its crisply-detailed exposed structure and exposed services, both of which were justified by the programme, was a significant architectural image of the 1980s and it was a building to which Tony Hunt contributed a great deal of design imagination.

His recollection of the completion of the INMOS building is interesting. For him it was 'an excitement' but also 'an anticlimax'. It seemed that there was now 'nothing to design that had the comparable excitement and challenge'.[29] This is the kind of feeling of anticlimax that follows the completion of any major project on which a great deal of creative effort has been expended. It is perhaps significant that INMOS was the last project by AHA in which Tony Hunt was involved personally with all the details of the design. In all subsequent projects he has been involved primarily with the concept, the detailed design being carried out by an office design team. Fortunately, a new interest presented itself in the form of the Patera project and this in turn was followed by the Schlumberger building. Both of these projects are described in chapter 4.

Fig. 2.9. The building for the Halley Base of the British Antarctic Survey, with its unusual service conditions and with the requirement for prefabrication, presented the type of challenge that the innovative engineers at Anthony Hunt Associates were happy to respond to. The final design consisted of four interconnected plywood tubes constructed from curved stressed-skin insulated plywood panels. Jamieson Associates, 1983.

Photo: J. Reid and J. Peck

Fig. 2.11. The Waterloo International Rail
Terminal, London, England. The brief for this
building, with its complex technical
requirements, presented the kind of challenge
that the combined talents and experience of
the Hunt and Grimshaw offices were
particularly well equipped to meet (see
chapter 6). Nicholas Grimshaw and Partners,
1988.

As ever at AHA, there was also something unusual going on and at this time it was a building for the Halley Base of the British Antarctic Survey (*Fig. 2.9*). The final version of the design of this building, which had, of course, to be prefabricated from lightweight components, consisted of four interconnected plywood tubes, 9 m in diameter, made up of a series of compression rings constructed from interlocking, curved, stressed-skin insulated plywood panels. Within each tube a two-storey structure, constructed of similar panels, housed living and sleeping accommodation, together with office and research facilities for a team of 18 men. The building was designed to sit on a floating ice shelf 175 m thick and the panel system was designed so that, when assembled as a cylinder, it could withstand the radial pressure exerted by snow.

The classic challenges for the structural engineer are the bridge, the very large (long-span) enclosure and the stadium. In the late 1980s, Tony Hunt was given the opportunity to work on the Don Valley Stadium in Sheffield for the World Student Games (*Fig. 2.10*) and a long-span enclosure, the International Rail Terminal at Waterloo in London (*Fig. 2.11*).

The Don Valley Stadium contract was won in an interview competition with five other competing engineering firms and was carried out in conjunction with Sheffield Design and Building Services as architects. The building consisted of a teflon-glass membrane supported on a cantilever mast-and-vierendeel arrangement.

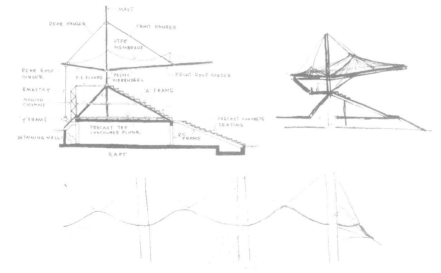

Tony Hunt

Fig. 2.10. The concept for the Don Valley Stadium, Sheffield. consisted of membranes supported on a tension-assisted steel framework to give optimum sight lines. Sketch of general arrangement by Tony Hunt. Sheffield Design and Building Services, 1990.

Tony Hunt's comments on this project provide a further insight into his preferred method of working:

'There were some special features to this project. It was designed in a series of three intensive 2–3 day sessions with an engineer and architect team all staying in a large house in the Derbyshire Dales, working as long a day and evening as we liked with no interruption — not even a telephone to disturb us. I have always believed that this saturation technique with total concentration, is the best way of approaching the concept design stage of any project. Flood the project with ideas bounced back and forth between the designers and the result will be a concept. Often it is unclear as to who actually designed what because the iterative process developed between the whole team.'[30]

The project involved the use of an interesting combination of materials – in situ and precast concrete, steel and the teflon-glass roof membrane — all appropriate to their various functions. The membrane, which was the largest in the UK at the time and the first in teflon-glass, was a real breakthrough for the firm.

'This, and the fact that the stadium was the first new one in use for years, made us experts on both membranes and stadium design.'[31]

The Waterloo International Terminal, described in detail in chapter 7, is the finest piece of railway station architecture to be produced in Britain since the termini of the great Victorian engineers. State-of-the-art techniques of computer-aided design were used in conjunction with the latest developments in steel construction to solve the problems posed by the very demanding site conditions.

A wide range of other work was also carried out in the 1980s. The firm continued to design large steel-frame buildings with finely crafted elements and joints, notable examples being the Amada Machine Tools Showroom in Kidderminster (Fig. 2.12) with the Glazzard Architects Co-operative, and a warehouse for Wiggins Teape at the Aztec West Industrial Park

Fig. 2.12. Amada Machine Tools Showroom, Kidderminster, England was executed in the vocabulary of exposed steelwork which AHA has refined throughout its entire existence. Glazzard Architects Co-operative.

Photo: Anthony Hunt Associates

with Aukett Limited as architects. Several membrane structures were also designed, including a series of short- and medium-span canopies for the Glasgow Garden Festival and a demountable theatre at Alton Towers. A major work in reinforced concrete was the Truro Crown Courts building with the architects Evans and Shalev.

By the late 1980s, with the Waterloo International Terminal and Don Valley Stadium underway and a number of prestigious projects recently completed, AHA was maintaining its position as one of the three leading structural engineering consultancies in the UK, with offices in Cirencester, London and Sheffield. At this point the firm took the momentous decision to become part of the YRM group — a large multi-disciplinary practice of architects, structural and services engineers. AHA had had tenuous links with YRM for several years prior to the establishment of the formal relationship. They had been involved in several competition entries

although they had never produced any built work together. In making the decision to merge they were to some extent conforming to current trends: it was a period in which many such amalgamations were occurring and two other organisations, in addition to YRM, were interested in taking over AHA at this time.

Tony Hunt anticipated several advantages of joining YRM. He hoped that it would allow easier growth because, in addition to its own client base, AHA would have access to YRM's clients. It would also provide opportunities for carrying out a wider scope of work, and for improving the management structure, and it gave AHA access to YRM's state-of-the-art CAD system.

The relationship between AHA and YRM, which was a public company of which Tony Hunt became a director, was complex. AHA took over the structure group of YRM and became an independent division of the company — one of five — and the company name was changed to YRM Anthony Hunt Associates. This meant that it retained its identity, something that was to prove invaluable when the YRM group failed in 1997.

Following the establishment of YRM AHA,

the centre of gravity of the firm was transferred to London with offices in Britton Street. The total staff complement was now around 140, spread between offices in London, Cirencester, Sheffield and Milton Keynes. This was the largest that it had ever been.

The years of association with YRM were to prove to be a period of mixed fortune. YRM had a number of large corporate clients, including the British Airports Authority, and therefore the potential to attract very large projects but, partly as a result of the recession in Britain in the early 1990s, this potential was not realised. Two notable examples of major projects that did not materialise are a railway station at Ashford, on the Channel Tunnel Rail Link, and a major new building for the BBC at White City in London.

A number of large competitions were entered, for example, for Terminal 5 at London's Heathrow Airport (*Fig. 2.13*) and Kuala Lumpur Airport, but without success. The Terminal 5 competition, which the whole YRM group was invited to enter and in which it came second, was a particular disappointment for Tony Hunt who still maintains that their proposal was the best and most exciting solution.

'*Here again a very small team worked*

Fig. 2.15. Factory for Dyson Appliances, Marlborough, England. The recently-developed technology which allowed hot-rolled steel sections to be given curved profiles was exploited here to produce an updated version of the Reliance Controls building. The sinusoidal curves of the roof improved weathertightness and enhanced structural efficiency. Chris Wilkinson, 1998.

Fig. 2.16. The roof cladding of the Dyson factory is capable of spanning between the sinusoidally-curved main elements. The lack of clutter in the way that the cladding and structural elements have been arranged recalls the Reliance Controls building of three decades earlier.

Photo: Anthony Hunt Associates

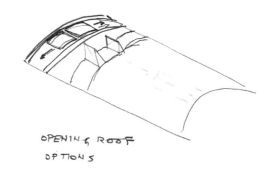

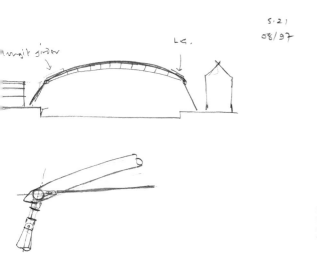

Fig. 2.17. Stuttgart 21, Hauptbahnhof. The sketches executed by Tony Hunt at the ideas stage of this competition entry give an insight into the 'thinking by sketching' method which is an important aspect of his approach to design. The final design won second prize in the competition. Wörner and Partner, 1997.

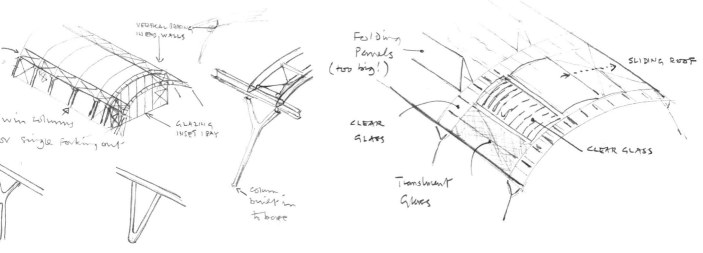

intensively and produced the solution from a range of options in a very short time. As with the Waterloo International Terminal and the Don Valley Stadium, it was an engineer's dream — long-span structures, lightweight, associated with aircraft but not aping their technology … light and technologically advanced.'[32]

The concept drawings for this project were carried out by Tony Hunt and several of these are illustrated in his *Sketchbook*.[33]

The failure of YRM to win competitions may have been due to the fact that they found it difficult to retain talented young staff. Tony Hunt

thought that this was because young designers were not permitted the freedom nor given the responsibility that their talent warranted. Senior management retained too tight a grip on projects and would not delegate design responsibility to younger people. YRM, with its top-heavy

Fig. 2.18. National Botanic Garden of Wales. This innovative single-layer dome is a toroidal form executed in one-way spanning tubular steel arches, of varying span, with orthogonal linking elements. Foster and Partners, 1999.

structure and highly-paid senior management, which had developed during the boom years of the 1980s, and with its corporate clients who by the early 1990s were feeling the pinch of recession, had begun to enact the classic scenario that would lead to financial collapse.

Throughout this period YRM AHA continued to attract interesting work on its own account, some of which was to prove to be as frustrating as the YRM work. For example, they were invited to become involved in the design of an international conference centre in Paris (*Fig. 2.14*). This was a massive project — one of President Mitterand's *grands projets* — which involved a group of three long-span buildings in steel and glass with a projected cost of £250 million. The competition-winning design, with the architect Francis Soler, remained unbuilt because the project was cancelled by the French Government. A positive outcome was that, by the time the project was abandoned, Tony Hunt had opened an office in Paris and this began to attract other work including a large office complex in Geneva and a Palais de Justice in Nanterre.

The association with YRM, which was described by Tony Hunt as 'a lean period in terms of interesting buildings',[34] was not without its successes. YRM AHA participated in five of the entries for the Museum of Scotland competition, including the winning scheme by Benson and Forsyth. The resulting building in Edinburgh, engineered by YRM AHA, is remarkable for the sculptural complexity of the form and for the very high quality of finish that was achieved with its partially exposed reinforced-concrete structure. The Cambridge Law Faculty building, with Foster and Partners, and the Lloyds Register of Shipping building, with the Richard Rogers Partnership, were begun at this time. The latter is notable for its unusual precast- and in situ-concrete composite structure.

The firm also completed an innovative factory design at Malmesbury for Dyson Appliances (Figs 2.15 and 2.16). This project was described by Tony Hunt as 'an extension of the basic idea on which the Reliance Controls building was based'.[35] Distinctive features of this building were the use of long-span roof cladding, which reduced the number of secondary elements that were required, and the adoption of a sinusoidal profile for the primary beams, which gave greater structural efficiency and better weather tightness than would have been possible with a flat roof.

A small, but unusual, structure was the West India Dock Footbridge in London, with Future Systems, a practice with which AHA had collaborated previously over a number of innovative projects none of which, unfortunately, was built. The distinctive feature of the bridge was that the multi-span structure was supported on a series of floating pontoons. This device had the advantage of eliminating a long span without creating the need for a series of expensive underwater foundations. The pontoon idea presented problems of vertical deflection under varying loads and horizontal drift due to wind but these were solved by ingenious arrangements of tension piles at each pontoon. The concept was a brilliant feat of lateral thinking. The 1990s were also notable for the large number of unbuilt projects involving Tony Hunt. A selection of these, which gives an indication of the range of his fertile imagination, is to be found in the recently published *Tony Hunt's Sketchbook*[36] (Fig. 2.17).

The YRM group failed in 1997 and six firms expressed an interest in acquiring its structures division. Tony Hunt, with five senior colleagues, was able to negotiate a management buy-out enabling the firm to regain its former identity and

Fig. 2.19. National Botanic Garden of Wales. The tubular arch elements spring from a perimeter concrete ring buried beneath a grassed landscape. Foster and Partners, 1999.

independence under its original title Anthony Hunt Associates. Most people who have worked with Tony Hunt feel that the link with YRM did not suit AHA. For example, John Young, of the Richard Rogers Partnership, said:

'I am not sure with hindsight whether the link up with YRM was ideal for a person like Tony. The corporate culture of YRM was not necessarily Tony's thing. He is now back doing what he enjoys best and is best at.'[37]

Similar sentiments were expressed by Nicholas Grimshaw in an interview with the author.

Anthony Hunt Associates emerged

remarkably unscathed from the association with YRM. Throughout this period it had continued to operate with its distinctive, very successful ethos intact. The firm currently employs around 60 people: there are six directors, six associates and approximately 40 senior engineers and technicians plus support staff. There are offices in Cirencester, London, Sheffield and Edinburgh.[38] The firm is structured into seven design teams each headed by a director or an associate. These teams usually consist of five or six persons and are more or less permanent in terms of personnel although they are adjusted depending on the size of the job in hand. Tony Hunt and one other

Fig. 2.21. Eden Project, Cornwall, England. Nicholas Grimshaw and Partners, 2000.

Fig. 2.20. Eden Project, Cornwall, England. Nicholas Grimshaw and Partners, 2000.

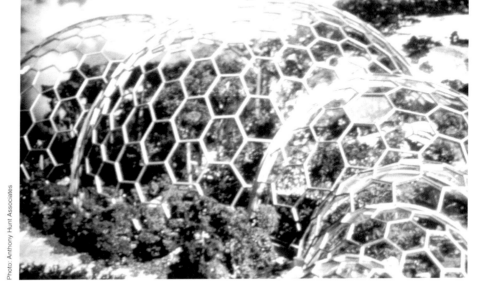

director, David Hemmings, are not members of design teams. Although still closely associated with both the architect and the engineering design teams, Hunt now concentrates on the conceptual stages of projects, usually for competition entries. If the entry is successful the design is handed over to one of the teams for development and execution. David Hemmings, who has been with Hunt since the early 1970s and who was very actively involved in most of the key early projects, such as the Willis, Faber and Dumas building, now acts as office manager with responsibility, among other things, for allocating jobs to design teams.

AHA entered the year 2000, approaching its fourth decade of existence, with its ethos and vitality intact and with a list of active projects reflecting the same mixture of work that it has always enjoyed. The firm is engaged on a core of projects that represent a competent professionalism together with a number of high profile projects with new and interesting challenges of architectural significance. The dome for the National Botanic Garden of Wales, with Foster and Partners (*Figs 2.18* and *2.19*), and the Eden project with Grimshaw (*Figs 2.20* and *2.21*), undoubtedly fall into the second category. A third strand of work consists of the unusual and the quirky. Currently there is a design for an all-glass bridge that is waiting for a suitable site.

Throughout its existence AHA has consistently produced engineering that is both visually satisfying and technically competent. It has the distinction of being the structural engineering consultant on two of only three Modern buildings which have been accorded Grade 1 listed status before the normal 30-year period from completion has elapsed (the Alexandra Road housing and the Willis, Faber and Dumas building). This work has been well publicised and has influenced a whole generation of architects and engineers.

Perhaps the most significant achievement of AHA has been its contribution to the redefinition of the relationship between architects and engineers. The influence that AHA has exerted has been driven by the personal agenda of Tony Hunt, the 'architect's engineer', who provides the means for new freedom of expression from the inception of a design to its ultimate refinement by close collaboration in a dynamic teamworking relationship.

Chapter Three
Hunt and Team 4

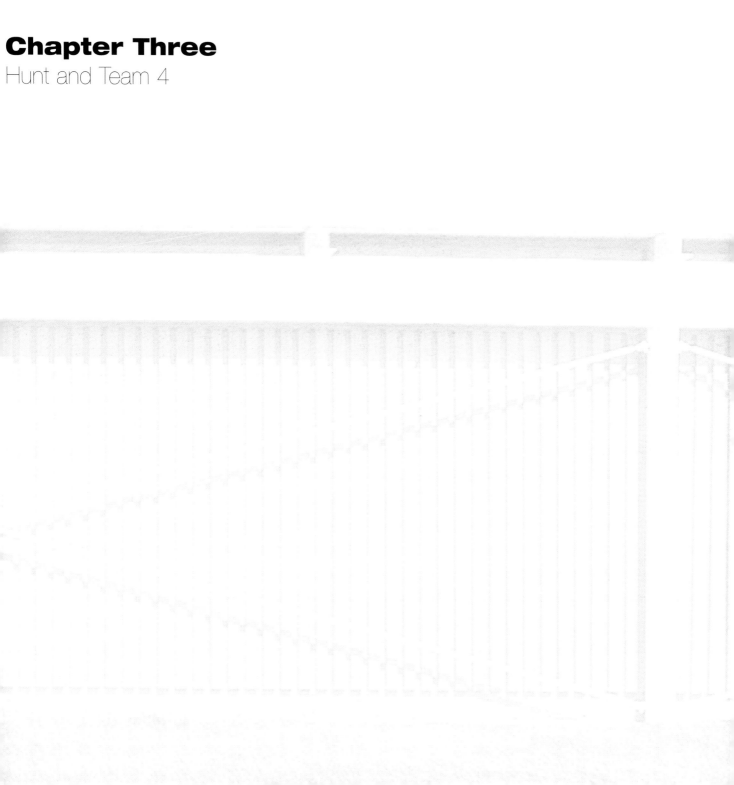

Chapter Three
Hunt and Team 4

Introduction

It was with Team 4 that Tony Hunt began the architect–engineer collaborations that would generate his unique contribution to modern building design. Team 4 consisted of Norman Foster, Richard Rogers and two architect sisters, Wendy Cheeseman, who subsequently married Foster, and Georgie Wolton. Rogers' wife Su, who was not an architect but who had studied Urban Design at Yale, was also closely involved. Three aspiring architects, Laurie Abbott, Frank Peacock and John Young joined the practice soon after its foundation. Team 4 was dominated, however, by the powerful architectural personalities of Foster and Rogers.

In the late 1950s, Richard Rogers studied architecture at the Architectural Association in London, then greatly under the influence of Peter Smithson. Norman Foster had a more conventional architectural education at Manchester University. Both went to Yale in 1961 where they completed masters degrees under Paul Rudolph and Serge Chermayeff. At that time, the USA held much that was of interest to anyone concerned with what was new and exciting in architecture. Louis Kahn was teaching at Philadelphia, and the buildings of Mies van der Rohe and Saarinen were still refreshingly new. Those of Frank Lloyd Wright, most of which Foster and Rogers visited, held many lessons. There was also an exciting architectural culture on the West Coast. The California Case Study Houses of Craig Ellwood and Ezra Ehrenkrantz's Schools Construction Systems Development project (SCSD)

Fig. 3.1. The Creek Vean House, Cornwall, England. Team 4.

were generating a lot of architectural interest at the time. Following the period at Yale, Richard and Su Rogers travelled to California, where Rogers worked for Skidmore, Owings and Merrill, and Foster spent some time with Richard Buckminster Fuller.

Throughout their formal architectural education, and immediately afterwards, Foster and Rogers were therefore directly exposed to the work of several of the principal figures then engaged in the process of redefining Modernism, following the exposure of the naiveties and inadequacies of much of the formalistic architecture of the first wave. It was a good time for this pair of high achievers, each driven by a powerful need to make a mark on the world through the medium of architecture, to be entering the field. They became friends at Yale and collaborated in Team 4 on their return from the USA in 1963.

The early work of Team 4 was on small-scale buildings, most of them private houses, and all the structural engineering was carried out by Tony Hunt. Two important commissions were a house at Creek Vean in Cornwall, England, for the parents of Su Rogers (Figs 3.1 and 3.2), and at Murray Mews in London, a series of three adjoining houses (Figs 3.3 and 3.4). Both of these projects were executed in loadbearing masonry and concrete, and were therefore significantly different in architectural character from the steel and glass buildings for which Rogers and Foster would subsequently become known. The young practice poured huge amounts of energy into these first, early design projects and, as is often the case with young architects, overloaded them with the architectural ideas that had been accumulating throughout their formal education.[39]

Considering that they were built by traditional methods, the buildings were unconventionally planned. The architects, due to a combination of inexperience, a high level of architectural aspiration, and an unwillingness to compromise, did not accept the restrictions, in the form of parallel arrangements of walls running continuously through all levels of the building, that are normally considered sensible with the loadbearing-wall method of construction.

The Creek Vean house was located on a steep-sided inlet off the Fal estuary in Cornwall, England. It was set *within* rather than *on* the landscape, being located below the top of a slope; flat roof surfaces were covered with vegetation which also grew freely on the steps which ran over and between the main parts of the building. Both of these features are reminiscent of buildings by Frank Lloyd Wright, whose influence is also seen in the free plan, in which a fan-shaped arrangement of walls allowed full advantage to be taken of the views across Pill Creek. The layouts of the Murray Mews houses were more regular, due to the restrictions of the site, and the plans were rectilinear, but the configurations of the interior spaces were complex, ingeniously planned and visually exciting.

Fig. 3.2. The Creek Vean House, Cornwall, England. Interior.

Photo: Anthony Hunt Associates

49

From a constructional viewpoint the buildings were eccentric. Significant variations in floor plan occurred between levels, which broke the continuity of loadbearing walls, and devices such as mezzanine floors, voids running the full height of the building and large areas of roof glazing were skilfully combined to allow top light to penetrate to the lowest levels. The resulting complexity made heavy demands on the support capability of the loadbearing-wall structures and required deft engineering from Tony Hunt, who used continuous in situ reinforced-concrete floor slabs for structural efficiency and integrity, and upstand beams to support upper-level structural walls which did not run through the lower storeys. Hunt also gave careful attention to the question of lateral stability. Rogers' and Foster's main architectural preoccupations in these designs were with issues of massing and space and light. They demanded a great deal from the technology of masonry and challenged its possibilities. Their challenge, however, was launched from a position of relative ignorance concerning the structural viability of the buildings. Tony Hunt set the limits and transformed into physical reality the design ideas that resulted from the highly sculptural approach to architecture that they were adopting at this stage in their development.

A notable feature of these early buildings was an absence of finishing materials, apart from the painting of the timber work. The walls of the Creek Vean house were of honey-coloured

Fig. 3.3. Murray Mews Houses, London, England.

Photo: John Donat

structural blockwork and the undersides of the floor slabs were fairfaced concrete. At Murray Mews the vocabulary was that of red brickwork and concrete. The armatures of the buildings were therefore laid bare in conformity with the then current fashion, pioneered in Britain by Alison and Peter Smithson, for employing the colours and textures of the basic materials, be they structural framework or blockwork partition, as ornamentation. It produced buildings which possessed a hint of the 'readability' which would become a feature of later work by both Foster and Rogers.

Readability, however, presented a problem, which was quality control; very high standards of finish were required. In masonry this implied straight, level courses and precise pointing; in concrete it meant well-finished formwork and complete compaction. All of these were dependent on craft skills, which, with the disappearance of the apprenticeship system in the 1950s and 60s, had become increasingly difficult to obtain in the industrialised world. For Foster and Rogers this problem would eventually be solved by the abandonment of traditional materials and an increasing reliance on the factory-made products, a move that would have a profound effect on their architectural style.

The Creek Vean and Murray Mews projects were successfully completed and drew much critical acclaim. They provided an excellent springboard for the young Team 4 practice. The buildings were also important for Tony Hunt. At Creek Vean and Murray Mews he realised in loadbearing masonry something which was very difficult to build in that medium, namely a multi-storey building with a free-form plan that varied significantly between levels. He did this, furthermore, with great subtlety and without recourse to structural gymnastics. The quality of the engineering went unnoticed by the uninitiated, however, including most architectural critics. What these observers saw was simply an interesting configuration of planes, volumes and light, effortlessly combined. This was no doubt the intention of the architects of Team 4, although they must also have been well aware of Tony Hunt's creative contribution to the success of these projects.

The buildings were therefore highly

significant for all involved although the cost in effort in completing these early house projects was enormous. The construction method required that much time be devoted to detailing and to the supervision of construction. In the early period of the existence of Team 4, six architects took two years to produce four small houses. For idealistic young architects this was too slow a method of transforming the world. It was also economically unsustainable.

'After having done these four houses it became apparent that we had to change our ways or we were going to go broke.'[40]

The constructional system used at Creek Vean and Murray Mews, and the architectural vocabulary it made possible, were therefore not destined to form the basis of further architectural development for either Foster or Rogers. Perhaps the most important role that these buildings played was that of the catalyst that stimulated fruitful and constructive working relationships between Foster and Rogers and Hunt.

Reliance Controls

It was the Reliance Controls building (*Fig. 3.5*), the last project that Foster and Rogers worked on together before Team 4 broke up in 1967, that pointed the way to the kind of architecture that was their original contribution to late twentieth-century Modernism. As with the earlier buildings, the contribution of Tony Hunt to this project was crucial to its success.

Fig. 3.4. Murray Mews Houses, London, England. Section showing the complex internal geometry.

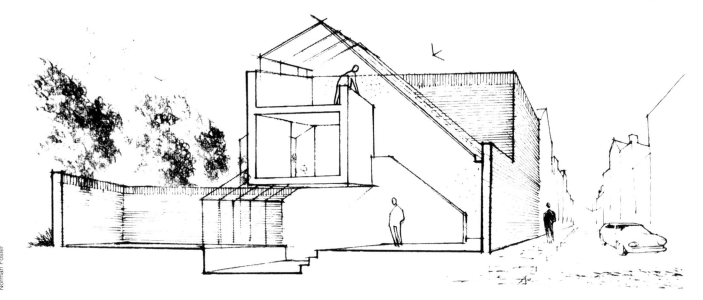

Chapter Three
Hunt and Team 4

In the first volume of the series of books that he edited on the Foster practice, Ian Lambot described the Reliance Controls building as occupying a pivotal position in the development of Norman Foster as an architect. The same was true of Richard Rogers; in his words: ' Reliance was a breakthrough. We had found our style'.[41] Lambot's comment on the significance of the building to Rogers was:

'To Richard Rogers Reliance was a matter of "...shaking off Yale ..." and with it the massy, sculptural east coast approach of Rudolph and Chermayeff, and taking on board the lighter influences he and Foster had experienced on the other coast of America: most notably due to the Case Study houses by Craig Ellwood and Ezra Ehrenkrantz's SCSD schools'.[42]

The Reliance Controls building differed from its predecessors in several respects. Team 4 was one of three practices recommended to the client by James Stirling, who wished to encourage and promote this promising young practice. It was also their first truly professional commission in the sense that it was for a client who was neither a relative nor a family friend and therefore devoid of the possible indulgence of inexperience that the latter situation might imply. It was with this commission, therefore, that the Team 4 practice came of age.

The building itself was a small factory to house the clean processes of component manufacture for the electronics industry: a type which was new in the experience of Team 4.

A third significant factor was the relative insensitivity, from a planning point of view, of the site which was located among small factories and warehouses of no particular architectural merit. This circumstance gave Team 4 much greater freedom over the general aesthetic treatment and choice of materials than had been the case with the house projects.

Other significant aspects of the brief were that the building was larger than anything that Team 4 had tackled before, that it was needed quickly and that the budget was tight. The last two of these required a different constructional system than had been used in the house projects. Creek Vean and Murray Mews had been literally manufactured on site out of masonry and reinforced concrete in a lengthy and laborious process that had been difficult to control. The requirements of the Reliance Controls brief forced a change of construction method so that the site operation became one of assembly of prefabricated components. This required a major design input into the development of neat ways of joining components together. Foster and Rogers found the aesthetic possibilities offered by this new approach much more congenial than had been their experiences with masonry and concrete. Tony Hunt was a very willing collaborator in this development. His comment on the change was 'this [Reliance Controls] was the building that allowed us to do what we wanted to do'.[43]

The project embraced several ambitions.

Foster, Rogers and Hunt wanted to take full control of all of the processes that would affect the appearance of the finished building, from preliminary design right through to completion. They also wanted to explore and develop the architectural ideas that currently interested them. Perhaps the most significant of these was the conviction that a truly Modern architecture could be created by making use of the mass-produced products of industry. One of the challenges for Team 4 was therefore to produce a successful architecture from 'found' components. The Case Study houses of Charles Eames, known to Hunt and actually seen by Foster and Rogers in America, were recent precedents for this approach. Their interest in the idea was reinforced by its connection with another idea that they shared with the early Modernists, the cost- and time-saving benefits of mass production.

Yet another early Modernist idea that influenced the design of the Reliance Controls building was a desire to make the building socially acceptable by eliminating all distinction between workforce and management in terms of the quality of the accommodation provision. This theme was to recur repeatedly in the work of both Foster and Rogers. Overriding all of these considerations was a desire to produce a building that represented a distinctively new approach to industrial architecture, which would maintain the career momentum built up with the earlier projects.

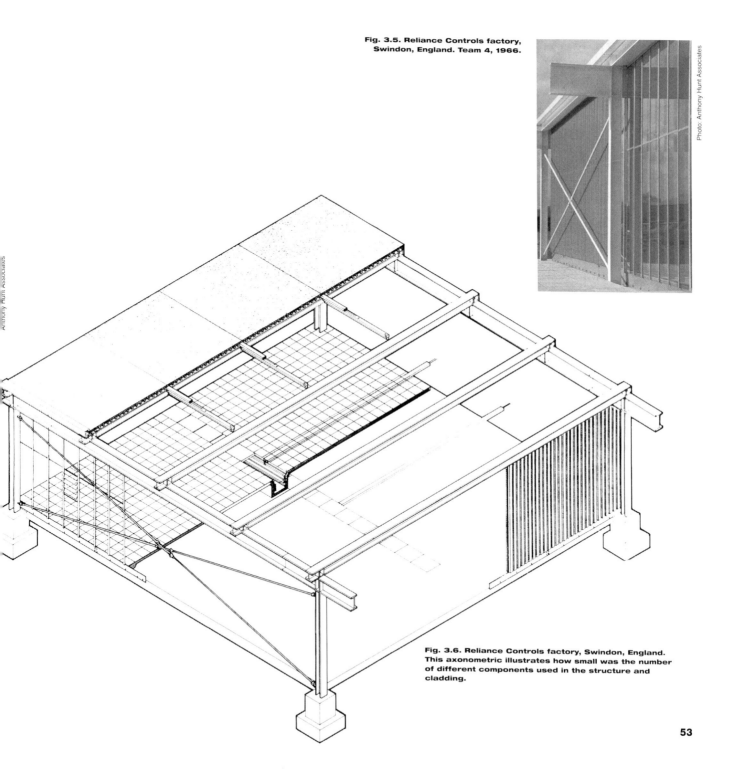

Photo: Anthony Hunt Associates

Fig. 3.5. Reliance Controls factory,
Swindon, England. Team 4, 1966.

Anthony Hunt Associates

Fig. 3.6. Reliance Controls factory, Swindon, England.
This axonometric illustrates how small was the number
of different components used in the structure and
cladding.

Reliance Controls manufactured components for the electronics industry. The brief for the factory called for 11000 m² of light industrial space (only the first phase of 3200 m² was actually completed by Team 4, although the building was subsequently extended under the direction of Foster Associates following the demise of Team 4) with provision for a variety of 'clean' activities, such as assembly and research areas, office accommodation, a staff restaurant and other amenities. There was also a requirement that the building should be capable of extension to allow for future expansion. As noted above the client called for very rapid completion of the project (ten months elapsed between the first client meeting and the handing over of the building) and there were strict financial constraints.

The general arrangement that emerged for the Reliance Controls building was very simple. It consisted of a single-storey shed measuring 160ft (48m) by 200ft (60m) on plan, subdivided internally by lightweight partitions, mostly of glass, with a central services spine sunk within the floor slab. In the original design scheme, internal courtyards, with fully-glazed walls, admitted natural light into the interior.[44] Above floor-slab level, the building was constructed entirely of industrially-made components and consisted essentially of non-structural wall and roof panels, either of glass or of profiled metal, supported by a steel-frame structure (Fig. 3.6).

The structure consisted of five, 5-bay portal

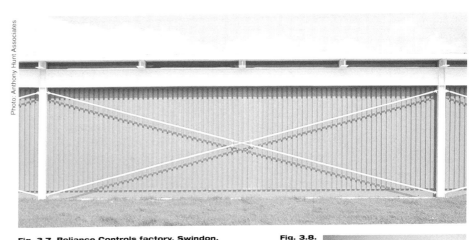

Fig. 3.7. Reliance Controls factory, Swindon, England. The cross-bracing in the side walls serves no structural purpose.

Fig. 3.8. Reliance Controls factory, Swindon, England. Column head detail showing purlins of Universal Column section.

frameworks of hot-rolled steel I-sections which ran the entire length of the building and which were placed 40ft (12m) apart. The bay size of the portals was also 40ft (12m) giving a 40ft (12m) square column grid. A secondary structure of hot-rolled H-sections at 10ft (3m) centres spanned between the portals and carried the profiled metal roof deck. These were pre-cambered to eliminate sag due to deflection. They were selected over the Universal Beam I-section primarily for aesthetic reasons. It was felt that the parallel-sided flanges of the Universal Column were more appropriate in this predominantly rectilinear building (Fig. 3.7 and Fig. 3.8).

The main frames were self-bracing in their own plane. Bracing in the across-building direction was by diagonal elements in the end

Fig. 3.9. Reliance Controls factory, Swindon, England. Interior.

walls acting in conjunction with the profiled-metal roof deck, which formed diaphragm bracing in the horizontal plane. Diagonal elements were also present in the side walls but these had no structural function (*Fig. 3.7*). They were included, at the insistence of Foster, for stylistic reasons. Tony Hunt was not happy with these pieces of unnecessary structure, which seemed to him to compromise the integrity of the design, but conceded that the building might have been 'too bland'[45] without them. The wall cladding consisted of a sandwich of profiled metal sheeting and polystyrene infill which spanned the 12ft (4m) between the floor slab and the roof structure in response to wind loading. The two skins did not act compositely but the configuration was, nevertheless, strong enough to eliminate the need for cladding rails. This greatly simplified the internal appearance of the walls.

To achieve continuity and a clean, uncluttered structure all structural connections were welded on site, following initial assembly by bolting. The columns were delivered to the site with stub beams attached and the site joints in the portals were at the points of contraflexure of the beam elements. The secondary beams were placed on top of the portals and welded to them. Butt joints between the secondary beams were also welded to make them continuous.

From a purely technical viewpoint, the structure stands up well to criticism. The choice of multi-span portal frames of I-section hot-rolled steelwork was entirely justified given the spans and loads involved, and the full continuity produced by the all-welded connections made possible slender, small-cross-section beam elements. The placing of the secondary beams above the primaries greatly simplified the construction process.

Such minor technical criticisms as can be made of the structure are mitigated by the need to satisfy aesthetic requirements. The pseudo bracing referred to above is one example. The placing of the perimeter columns and beams outside the walls of the building was another. This increased the potential maintenance costs by exposing the structure to the elements and also complicated the detailing of the roof-to-wall junction. It was not, therefore, desirable from a technical point of view.

There was a practical justification for the exposure of the structure, which was the expectation that the building would have to be extended at a later stage. The positioning of the perimeter structure outside the walls was intended to allow the extensions to be built without disturbing the skin of the original building — the new structure would be attached to the existing steelwork and the extension completed without any disruption of the interior. This did in fact take place, and when the building was extended, the final operation was one of dismantling the original cladding and repositioning it at the new edge of the building — a wonderful, and rare, example of planned flexibility actually being implemented.

Chapter Three
Hunt and Team 4

The Reliance Controls building attracted much positive critical attention following its completion and was awarded the first Financial Times Industrial Architecture Award and the Architectural Design Project Award. It was a significant milestone in the careers of the principal designers because it drew the attention of the architectural establishment to the fact that they were realising several of the aspirations of architectural Modernism.

There were in fact two broad respects, one socio-political and one aesthetic, in which the Reliance Controls building represented a re-examination of Modernist ideas. The first of these, the socio-political, had three aspects: one was the development of a particular kind of relationship with the client; another was the use of a building as a vehicle for social engineering and a third was the idea of flexibility. The aesthetic agenda also had two more closely related aspects, which were the making of architecture out of 'found' components — the products of industry — and a concern to develop an aesthetic that was celebrative of industry and technology.

The relationship which the architects established with the client, and the fact that this allowed them to modify the brief significantly, was important because it made possible a completely fresh approach to the planning of an industrial building. The way of working that Team 4 adopted at Reliance Controls would become a characteristic of the subsequent practices of both Foster and Rogers. Typically, clients would approach them

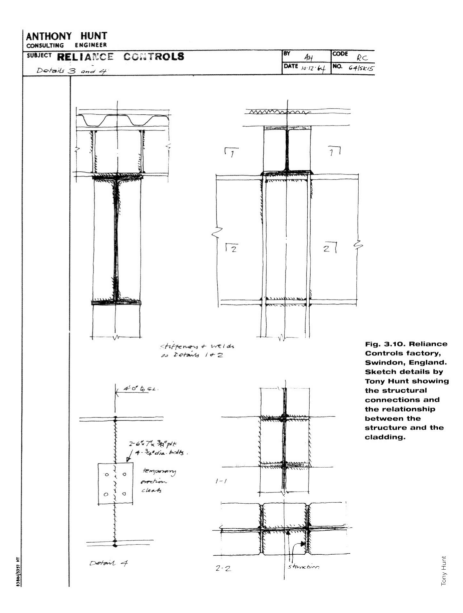

Fig. 3.10. Reliance Controls factory, Swindon, England. Sketch details by Tony Hunt showing the structural connections and the relationship between the structure and the cladding.

Tony Hunt

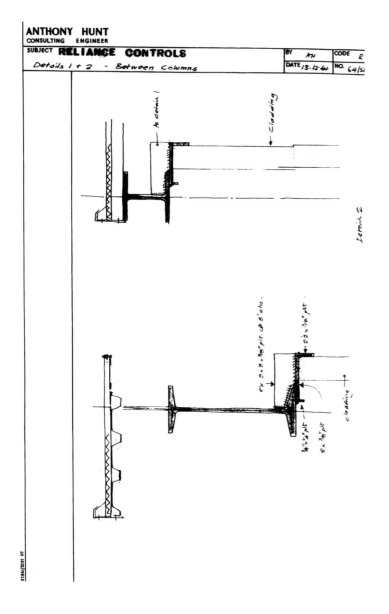

ANTHONY HUNT
CONSULTING ENGINEER

SUBJECT **RELIANCE CONTROLS**

Details 1 + 2 — Between Columns

BY AH CODE R

DATE 13.12.64 NO. 64/51

with a pre-determined solution to the problem of their building requirements that would be almost guaranteed to produce a building that would be, if not banal, certainly dull. Foster or Rogers would then persuade the client to do something quite different, and would so transform the project that the resulting building became a work of architecture that was intended, on the one hand, to enrich the daily lives of its users, and on the other, to give to the client a building that would enhance its reputation. In many cases they contrived to do this without exceeding the original budget.

An example of this way of working was the brief given to Foster for the IBM Pilot Head Office (see chapter 4), where he was asked to select a suitable off-the-peg system of portable buildings and plan the arrangement of these on the site. Foster persuaded IBM that a distinctive, one-off building could be produced at no extra cost, and the highly successful building that resulted, in which many of the ideas that had been tried at Reliance Controls were reused and developed, was the first of several important works produced by the Foster practice in the 1970s. As will be shown, Hunt made a major contribution to this building.

The Reliance Controls design was basically a single-envelope enclosure — one of several that would subsequently be produced by Foster and Rogers — and this configuration contributed to the social engineering possibilities of the design. By locating accommodation for diverse activities (production, office, amenities) within a single envelope and eliminating hierarchical arrangements of space, the architects expressed the idea of social equality and industrial democracy. They avoided the traditional arrangement of British industrial buildings — 'a management building standing separately in front of an industrial shed'[46] — and treated all types of accommodation equally. There was a common entrance lobby for workers and management with identical doors leading to the office and production areas. The expression of egalitarian ideas was to be developed subsequently and independently by both Foster and Rogers.

The idea of flexibility was another socio-political feature of the design that was to recur in subsequent work. All of the designers involved at Reliance Controls were interested in creating a building that was adaptable and extendable.[47] They also sought to achieve flexibility during the design and construction process to cope with a changing brief. One of the lessons of Murray Mews had been that, such is the length of time involved in producing a building, the requirements of the client tend to change between the initial commissioning and the final completion of the project. This is especially the case with buildings produced for rapidly-expanding industries, such as microelectronics. This experience led to the idea that a design should be made so that changes in the user requirements could be accommodated even during the construction stages — the ultimate ideal of Modernist functionalism. The single-envelope enclosure, subdivided by

lightweight partitions, which is what the Reliance Controls building was, was ideally suited to this objective.

At Reliance Controls, Foster, Rogers and Hunt explored the idea of making a building from industrially-produced components that were simply assembled on site, and with the prospect of minimising the 'wet-trade' activity associated with materials such as concrete and plaster. Tony Hunt, in particular, liked the idea of a building that was a 'kit of parts', with as few types of part as possible. Perhaps the purest version of this which he was involved with was the Patera Building (see chapter 6) which he designed with Michael Hopkins.

At Reliance Controls the minimisation of component types was achieved to a remarkable degree with the structure, which was reduced by Hunt to one type of column, two types of beam and a bracing element (*Fig. 3.6*). The elimination of the need for cladding rails, through the development of a wall-panel system that was capable of spanning from the floor slab to the roof structure, contributed to this minimisation. The elimination of bracing elements in the roof plane was also significant and was made possible by the use of the profiled metal roof deck as horizontal-plane diaphragm bracing. Tony Hunt recalls that this was achieved by providing many more fastening elements between the roof deck and the structure than would normally have been required, but admits that the ability of the roof to act as a diaphragm in response to wind loading was untested:

'These were the days when things could be done by the seat of the pants. We would not get away with this kind of thing today.'[48]

In other words, the system did not comply with received wisdom, as documented in building standards, but was judged by its designer, correctly, to be satisfactory.

The high level of simplicity in the structure and cladding was crucial to the aesthetics of the Reliance Controls building (*Fig. 3.9*). So also was the placing of the perimeter structure outside the building's envelope. The visual justification for this, as opposed to the practical reason mentioned above, was that it allowed 'a visual statement to be made of what the structure was'.[49] The highly mannered visual treatment of the structure (exposure, projection of beams beyond perimeter columns, redundant cross-bracing) was crucial to the design strategy. This, together with the fact that the building was made from readily available industrially-made components, which were combined in a seemingly effortless way to produce a coherent and elegant aesthetic, was what gave the building its visual quality. These attributes ensured that the Reliance Controls building became a pioneering work that would influence industrial architecture for the next three decades.

With this building Foster and Rogers reached a turning point that led to their each developing an individual and characteristic architectural style that was celebrative of the positive aspects of technology and industry. These characteristics were a 'readable' building with an exposed structure, good proportions, extreme neatness and clarity in both the overall concept and in the detailing, and the employment of a visual vocabulary of steel and glass components.

The visual success of the Reliance Controls building was its most important aspect. Such are the priorities of the architectural world that, no matter how great had been its other qualities, (in respect of social democracy, flexibility, the use of found components, etc.), the building would have gone virtually unnoticed by the architectural establishment if it had been visually unexciting. In architectural circles, appearance tends to be, if not quite all, certainly the prime consideration, with worthiness following far behind.

Although the design evolved through a genuine team effort, the contribution of Tony Hunt to the visual success of the Reliance Controls building, and therefore to the rise to prominence of Norman Foster and Richard Rogers, cannot be underestimated. The high degree of refinement of the exposed structure and the almost total lack of clutter in the building fabric were extremely important aspects of his achievement. The creation of the very neat wall-to-floor and wall-to-roof junctions, which were so crucial to the overall effect was another such aspect. For evidence of Hunt's substantial role in the detailing of the building, one need look no further than his many sketch drawings of the project (Fig. 3.10).

Team 4 was significant for British architecture for a number of reasons. Firstly, it established the reputations of Foster and Rogers as leading members of the new generation of architects. Virtually all of the buildings that Team 4 designed attracted the interest of the critics and were published in the architectural media, and the Reliance Controls building, in particular, was seen as an important reassessment of the architecture of the factory. Secondly, it brought into focus a number of ideas that would be developed independently by Foster and Rogers, taking slightly different directions as their work matured. Thirdly, it was with Team 4 that Foster and Rogers developed a working relationship with Tony Hunt. This was probably of more significance to Foster who, in the 1970s, went on to create two seminal buildings (Willis, Faber and Dumas and the Sainsbury Centre) with Hunt. It was less significant for Rogers, who worked with other engineers in the 1970s on the projects that would bring him international recognition.

Team 4 was important for Tony Hunt because it allowed him to work in an environment in which his engineering skills were challenged to produce extremely elegant engineering solutions to difficult problems raised by aesthetic requirements. This collaboration set the pattern for three decades of innovative activity in architectural engineering.

Chapter Four
Hunt and Foster

Chapter Four
Hunt and Foster

Introduction

Norman Foster is surrounded by an aura that causes his role in architecture to be described by critics and commentators only in superlatives. In the catalogue of the exhibition 'Six Architects', which was part of the Fifth International Biennale of Architecture in Venice in 1991, Colin Amery referred to Foster as representing 'the most advanced clarification of the application of science and modern technology to architecture we have seen in recent decades',[50] and, in his introduction to the same Biennale catalogue, Fulvio Irace described him as 'the "white knight" of Anglo-Saxon Modernism'.[51]

Foster is unquestionably a Modernist: he is an unashamed optimist with a stated belief in the idea of technology as a benign instrument of human progress. He is also single-mindedly dedicated to the application of this belief in an architectural context whether in actuality or symbolically, occasionally both. Typically, his buildings are affairs of pristine cladding supported by exquisitely detailed structure and enclosing diagrammatically perfect plans that are sensitive to human values and which serve the cause of equitably shared resources and accommodation within the workplace. Visually, they are precious objects in every respect:

'He transforms the ordinary and the everyday by his knack of treating industrial building materials like jewellery, and by his commitment to an unassertive polished elegance'.[52]

This chapter explores the role of Tony Hunt in the creation of the buildings that brought Foster to this position of deserved prominence and acclaim.

Foster Associates was founded in 1967 by Norman and Wendy Foster. In the early days they operated from the living room in Wendy Foster's flat that had also been the office of Team 4. Initially, the practice was desperately short of work, despite the very favourable publicity and exposure that followed the completion of the Reliance Controls building in 1966, and less resolute individuals might easily have surrendered their independence and become employees in other, better-established practices. As it was, they considered moving abroad 'to a more receptive and open society'.[53] They hung on, however, and the well-deserved break for the Fosters came with two projects in Britain that allowed them to develop the ideas that had come together at Reliance Controls. These were the Fred Olsen Amenity Centre in London's Millwall Dock and the IBM Pilot Head Office at Cosham. A number of small, but significant, projects followed in which the distinctive tone of the practice was consolidated, and the climax of this early period came towards the end of the 1970s with the completion of two outstanding buildings, the Willis, Faber and Dumas building in Ipswich and the Sainsbury Centre for the Visual Arts at Norwich. These established Foster as one of the leading architects of his generation. In the 1980s, buildings such as the Hong Kong and Shanghai Bank Headquarters in Hong Kong would project Foster Associates on to the world stage.

By the late 1990s, the firm, which by this time had become Foster and Partners, was enjoying an international reputation for design excellence and was carrying out high profile work in Europe, Asia and North America, operating from six offices located in Britain, continental Europe and Asia. Currently, the practice is run by a board of 11 directors, chaired by Norman Foster, who are responsible for design control, office management and financial control; 16 project directors manage a number of projects each and 35 associates run the projects on a day-to-day basis. That this scale of operation has been built up in 30 years from a starting point of a husband-and-wife team working from their living room says much for the single-mindedness with which Norman and Wendy Foster, and later Norman Foster alone,[54] pursued their goals and for the quality of the work that the practice has produced.

The quantity of work has been large and a very high proportion of it has been widely published. A remarkable feature of this body of work is the range and variety of visual expression that is encompassed. There is no single, distinctive Foster style; no set of images which together make a building instantly recognisable as being by Foster. One of the achievements of the practice was the creation of 'style-less' architecture, a goal of Modernism rarely realised by its early masters. This achievement was well summed up by Rayner Banham, who pointed

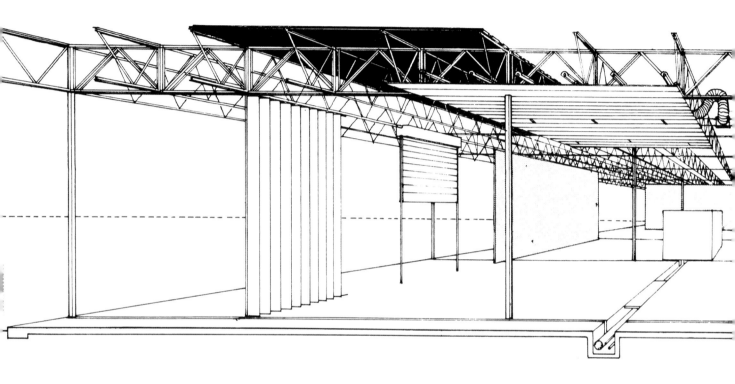

out[55] that the objective of Foster Associates was not so much the realisation of a distinctive style as the doing of what was appropriate in a stylish way.

'Appropriateness' is a key word, perhaps *the* key word in any assessment of Foster's architecture because the search for the appropriate architectural solution has been central to the ambitions of Foster Associates and Foster and Partners. It encompasses not just the idea that the client's needs should be satisfied but also the idea that the needs of society in general should be met. A building has therefore to be appropriate in respect of a number of aspects: its function, its context, the wellbeing of those who would use it and its consumption of resources. This is the explanation for the lack of visual connection between the many different buildings that the Foster practices have produced: each project was allowed to find its own visual expression in the course of the search for appropriateness.

Fig. 4.1. Newport School, Wales. Competition entry showing the combined structural and services zone at roof level and the demountable cladding and internal partition systems.

The quest for appropriateness implies a working methodology that has two key aspects. Firstly, there is the need for a thorough examination of the client's needs. Foster's approach therefore involves an initial process in which the problem is scrutinised in the widest possible context and the brief developed accordingly. The ways in which the briefs for two early projects, the Fred Olsen Amenity Centre and the IBM Pilot Head Office, were developed are good examples of this, but the methodology has been applied to all projects. Secondly, there is a recognition that all aspects of the design and realisation of a building (planning, structure, services, finance, etc.) must be accorded an appropriate level of priority. This is accomplished through teamwork between the architects and the specialist consultants involved. As was stated in a monograph that Foster and Partners produced in 1997 to publicise the work of the practice:

'Architecture is a mysterious process but it cannot be generated without the intimate collaboration between the client and a whole array of specialist skills. Orchestrating these skills is the architect's role.'[56]

An insight into Foster's personal approach to the issue of teamwork was given in his contribution to volume 1 of the series of books edited by Lambot.[57] He drew an analogy between designing a building and piloting a helicopter. He identified four controls that are employed for the latter. The *cyclic* is a vertical lever in front of the pilot which when moved forward or back or from side to side causes the helicopter to move in the same direction. To the left of the pilot is a horizontal lever, the *collective*, which, when moved up or down, will cause the helicopter to climb or descend. The *grip* of the collective is a third control because it can be twisted to adjust the power being delivered by the engine. Finally, *rudder pedals* allow the craft to be rotated about its vertical axis to change its direction. The control input to produce one type of movement affects the others. If the cyclic is pushed forward to move the aircraft forward, the machine will also descend unless the collective and power are adjusted. To fly the machine smoothly the pilot has to operate the controls in a co-ordinated way and this has to be done by 'feel', developed from practice, rather than by consciously thinking about what to do.

Thus it is with design, according to Foster. If changes are made to one aspect of a building (massing, materials, inside, outside, structure, heating, etc.) some or all of the other aspects will be affected. In architecture, however, a team of specialists is required to 'pull the different levers' and they must share a common vision and operate collectively towards a common goal, each respecting the other's creative input. In Foster's words:

'The architect is not handing down from above, passing the parcel to the specialists who wait in line to be told what to do. Each individual has the potential for a creative input.'[58]

The synergy that operates between the individual members of a design team is the equivalent of the 'feel' that is required to pilot a helicopter, and one of Foster's most significant skills is an ability to create the circumstances in which that synergy can develop. Foster's is very much a 'hands-on' approach. He insists on some personal involvement in all of the design teams that operate in the office at any given time. His commitment to this approach is also reflected in the layout of the office, which consists of long rows of tables with each designer, including Foster, having the same amount of work space.

Foster Associates therefore evolved a methodology of teamwork that is rare in architecture. The idea of teamwork between specialists, of course, became increasingly important in the twentieth century as buildings became more complex but few architects have made it work in the way that has been achieved by Foster. His success in this area is part of the explanation of the evolution of the stylish but style-less architecture that has come to characterise his work.

The methodology of teamwork that has been so crucial to the success of Foster Associates was developed in the early years of the practice. 'Much of what we now take for granted as architects is made explicable by the strivings of these early years'.[59] Volume 1 of the Lambot series, which deals with the period 1964 to 1973 and therefore with Team 4 and the earliest of the projects of Foster Associates, was the third volume to be published[60] but Norman Foster predicted that volume 1 would generate the most excitement[61] because it dealt with the period in which the working methodology that was the basis of the success of the practice came into being. This gives an indication of the importance that Foster himself attached to the early years.

All structural engineering for the early projects of Foster Associates was carried out by Tony Hunt, who has described the regular design meetings that were the principal vehicles for the realisation of a design in the following way:

'... a process in which everyone draws and scribbles away; people make suggestions, others take them up and develop them; eventually you get to the point where you cannot think any more; so you go away to think. Gradually the design evolves.'[62]

Tony Hunt was in at the beginning and was an important collaborator in the development of the working methodology that would become the

Fig. 4.2. Newport School, Wales. Competition entry, plan showing the spinal zone for services and circulation with classroom and other accommodation arranged on either side.

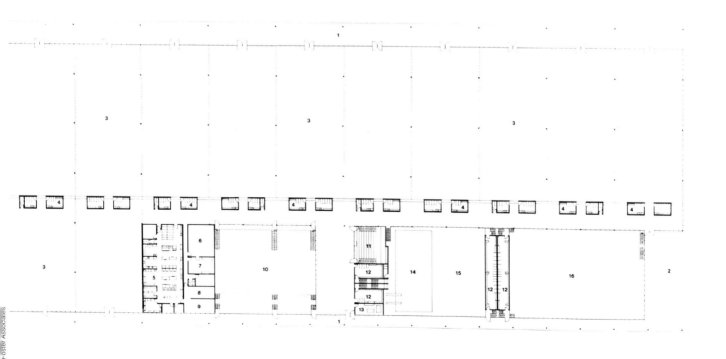

hallmark of the Foster practices. His primary role, that of the structural engineer, was to ensure that the engineering was 'appropriate'; to satisfy this requirement it had to be satisfactory both technically and visually. His other role was as a member of the design team; to fulfil this he had to contribute to a collective effort in a creative way, with the combination of assertiveness and willingness to compromise that that implied. Tony Hunt's visual sense, and his sympathy for the concerns of the architect, were a crucial part of this process.

The buildings that Foster Associates designed in the 1970s — the most crucial decade for the practice — fall into three categories: single- envelope enclosures, single-volume sheds and a multi-storey office.

The single-envelope enclosure

Throughout the 1970s the Foster office worked on a series of buildings which were configured similarly to the Reliance Controls factory. These included a competition entry for the design of a new comprehensive school (the Newport School)[63], a building for Computer Technologies, a pilot head office for the IBM company, a factory for Scendinaviska Aluminium Profiler AB (SAPA) and a school for handicapped children. They were all flat-roofed, deep-plan single-storey buildings in which diverse types of accommodation were located within a building envelope of simple rectangular plan. All were based on lightweight steel structures, clad in glass or metal, and all had easily demountable internal walls for flexibility in planning and use. They were made to tight budgets but money saved by the use of simple and repetitive structural and cladding systems was put to good use to fit out the interiors with carpets and other quality fittings.

The key ideas which informed the designs of these buildings were the same as those that had operated at Reliance Controls and were the following: the enclosure of all functions within a single envelope of simple shape; flexibility, in use and during the design and construction processes; and the use of standard, mass-produced components, for speed and economy of construction.

The first major project that Foster Associates worked on following its foundation in 1967 was a design competition for a comprehensive school at Newport in Wales (*Figs 4.1 and 4.2*). This has been described[64] as one of the most important buildings the practice never built, because it was with this project that the ideas which had informed the design of the Reliance Controls building were developed and refined. It was the knowledge gained in the Newport School competition that allowed the early built projects that followed to be accomplished in incredibly short time spans and to very tight budgets.

The essential features of the scheme for the Newport School building were a single-storey deep-plan enclosure supported by a lightweight steelwork structure. The plan was logical and was based on a spinal corridor which separated teaching areas on one side of the building from a strip of other accommodation including a lecture hall, an assembly hall, a sports hall, a swimming pool, kitchens, plant rooms and stores, on the other side. The perimeter walls, set back from the edge of the roof for shade, created a circulation route running around the entire perimeter of the building.

The design was heavily influenced by the prototype SCSD (Schools Construction Systems Development) building that Ezra Ehrenkrantz had built in California in 1964. It consisted of a modularised steel framework supporting lightweight walls and with a combined structure and services zone at roof level. The arrangement was intended to allow great flexibility in the use of space. It was to have been constructed from industrially-made components and the designers sought to minimise the number of separate components to produce an enclosure which was simple and quick to erect.

The structure of the Newport School was a grid of primary and secondary elements with the primary elements arranged as multi-bay portal frameworks spanning 40 ft (12·2 m) between 6 in. by 6 in. (15·24 cm by 15·24 cm) hollow-section columns. The portals were spaced 56 ft (17·07 m) apart and secondary elements, at 8 ft (2·44 m) centres, spanned between them. The primary and secondary elements were triangulated trusses of equal depth (4 ft/1·22 m) providing a combined structural and services zone with a flat top and bottom. Rigid joints between the beam and column elements eliminated the need for diagonal bracing in the walls.

The roof decking was a standard profiled metal system topped by 1 in. (2·54 cm) thick expanded polystyrene and felt. The foundation was a 6 in. (15·24 cm) thick reinforced raft, thickened to 12 in. (30·48 cm) under the columns. The perimeter walls and internal partitions were fixed to the floor slab and the underside of the roof structure.

As at Reliance Controls, Tony Hunt produced a structure that was reduced to a minimum number of different components, in this case two beam types and a single column type. The general arrangement was virtually identical to the Reliance Controls structure, the only significant difference being that triangulated elements were used in place of solid-web beams. This allowed the achievement of longer spans and also the creation of the combined structural and services zone under the roof.

A very high degree of flexibility was envisaged for the use of space. The lightweight internal partitions were demountable and even the doors in the perimeter walls could be moved easily. The services zone allowed changing requirements for environmental control and electrical services in the served spaces to be accommodated easily. A spinal duct in the floor slab, for wet and waste services with a plug-in facility, made it possible to relocate functions, such as lavatories, without difficulty. The internal arrangement could have been configured as a traditional school, with

Fig. 4.3. IBM Pilot Head Office, Cosham, England. Exterior.

Photo: Anthony Hunt Associates

classrooms and corridors, but many other arrangements, that would have facilitated different teaching approaches, would also have been possible. The building could also have been reconfigured to meet differing requirements on several time scales (day-to-day, weekday–weekend, term–vacation) and thus to meet the needs of the whole community that it served.

Sadly, the Newport scheme did not win the design competition and was not built. Its significance for Foster Associates was that it provided the opportunity for the set of architectural ideas that had informed the design of the Reliance Controls building to be developed and refined. These ideas would find expression, almost immediately, in the design that Foster

Associates created for the IBM Pilot Head Office at Cosham.

The Pilot Head Office at Cosham (*Fig. 4.3*) was intended to serve as a temporary UK main office for the IBM company and was located on a site adjacent to one on which a permanent headquarters building for IBM UK was already under construction. When the design was commissioned IBM, in common with many rapidly-expanding companies at the time, was making significant use of clusters of timber-framed portable buildings and envisaged that this type of accommodation would be the most suitable for the temporary head office. Foster Associates were therefore instructed to report on the most suitable of the proprietary systems then available and to advise on the disposition of the buildings on the site. This possibility was indeed considered, but the solution which Foster recommended was that of a custom-designed building based on lightweight industrialised components, similar in principle to the Newport School building, and it was this scheme that was finally executed.

The brief called for adaptable accommodation because at the time of commissioning the detailed use of the building could not be specified precisely. It was envisaged that it would house 750 employees initially but that provision should be made for the expansion of this number to 1000. This suggested a gross floor area of 150 000 ft^2 (14 000 m^2) with possible expansion to 200 000 ft^2 (18 600 m^2).

There was also a requirement, inevitable given that the company expected to occupy the building for a relatively short period, that the cost of construction should be minimised and that the building be erected very quickly.

The ideas for the IBM building were developed using the same methodology that had proved so successful at Reliance Controls. Regular intensive design meetings were held in which all aspects of the design were discussed. Three types of accommodation (office, amenity and a large computer room) were required. The conventional approach would have been to house these in different buildings. At Cosham these were all placed within a single envelope which would preserve flexibility, provided that the services and environmental control systems were correspondingly flexible. The scheme devised for Newport School, with its single-storey steel framework, demountable walls and roof services zone, satisfied these requirements.

Due to the need to compete with the portable building alternative on cost and speed of erection, and to the fact that the ground conditions were poor because the site was a former landfill rubbish tip, technical considerations exerted a major influence on the design. That of the structure was particularly crucial to the success of the project. Tony Hunt considered using long piles (40 ft - 12·2 m) to reach firm strata but this would have meant reducing the number of separate foundations to a minimum and the resulting long-span structure

would have been slow to erect and expensive to produce. The alternative was to use a short-span structure in conjunction with a rigid raft foundation that would 'float' on the low-bearing-capacity substrata. A number of such systems were considered, including one that was based on solid-web I-sections, similar to those used at Reliance Controls. The favoured system was in fact similarly configured to the Reliance Controls structure, but with lightweight triangulated girders in place of solid-web beams creating the combined structure and services zone at roof level that was crucial to the provision of the required flexibility in the use of space.

Tony Hunt wrote a performance specification for this structure that imposed a strict time schedule and financial limits, and several steel fabricators tendered for the contract. It was awarded finally to Metsec, which proposed a modified version of its proprietary system of cold-formed triangulated steel joists as the basis of the structural design. In the final version the structure was reduced to two beam types, each 600 mm deep, and one square hollow-section column type. A 7·5 m square column grid was adopted with secondary beams at 2·5 m centres supporting an insulated profiled-metal roof deck (*Fig. 4.4*).

The only significant departure from the standard, mass-produced Metsec arrangement was that the lower booms of the girders were carried through to the columns to form rigid beam-to-column joints. This made the frame self-bracing,

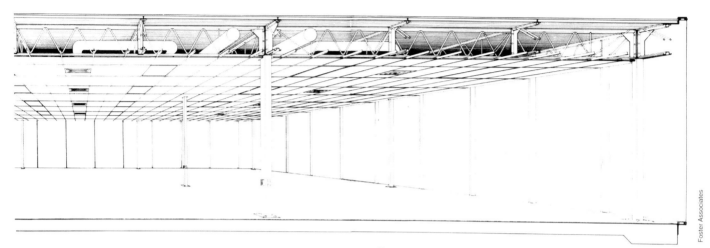

Fig. 4.4. IBM Pilot Head Office, Cosham, England. Perspective showing combined structure and services zone at roof level similar to the Newport School scheme.

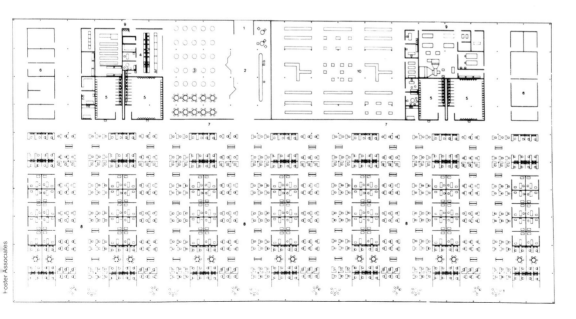

Fig. 4.5. IBM Pilot Head Office, Cosham, England. Plan showing offset circulation dividing production area from the cafeteria and other support facilities.

Chapter Four
Hunt and Foster

Photo: Anthony Hunt Associates

Fig. 4.6. IBM Pilot Head Office, Cosham, England. Interior showing perimeter circulation zone with desks clear of direct sunlight.

and eliminated the need for diagonal bracing in the walls. Diagonal bracing was provided in the roof plane to hold the building square in response to asymmetrical wind loading.

The perimeter walls were fully glazed and easily-movable lightweight partitions were used to subdivide the interior. The building was fully air-conditioned, with the air-conditioning units sited externally, on the roof, above the columns. Hot air ducts ran as required in the services zone between the ceiling and the roof deck and this space also served as a plenum for return air. Electrical and telephone services were routed in the roof space and were conducted to floor level through the square hollow-section structural columns.

The accommodation arrangement (Fig. 4.5) was similar to that envisaged for the Newport

School. A spinal corridor separated the open-plan office from the computer room and amenity areas, and a perimeter zone (Fig. 4.6), now within the external wall, was used as a circulation route — an arrangement that would be repeated at the Willis, Faber and Dumas building.

The IBM Pilot Head Office was remarkably successful in almost every respect. It provided the client with a distinctive, stylish building which was enjoyable in use for all grades of employee and which was undoubtedly a preferable solution to the client's requirements than the assemblage of proprietary portable buildings that they had originally envisaged. That this was achieved within the original budget and timescale says much for the growing professional competence of the Foster office and their consultants. A measure of the success of the building was that, although it had been intended as temporary accommodation to last for a period of three to four years, it was retained by the company, following the completion of the permanent head office, and converted for use as an independent research unit.

The building was remarkable in an architectural sense for the extent to which it adhered to the ideals of Modernism. Perhaps its most distinctive feature was that it was made entirely from mass-produced proprietary components. It has been described as a twentieth-century Crystal Palace[65] — and it actually achieved the kind of relationship between architecture and industry which has often been claimed, erroneously, for other steel and glass buildings, especially of the High Tech style.

The choice of the lightweight Metsec steelwork system was crucial to the success of the IBM building. At Reliance Controls the elements were standard I-beams but much effort of a one-off, handcrafted nature had been required to fashion the very neat joints between the various elements that contributed to the visual success of that building. The structure of the IBM building was a straightforward assemblage of standard Metsec components (*Fig. 4.7*). This was both inexpensive and allowed the structure to be rapidly erected on site using no plant larger than a fork-lift truck. The resulting speed and economy was what made the building competitive with the alternatives.

The project was a very important one for Foster Associates, not only because it was very successful, but also because it occurred at a crucial stage in the development of the firm and was being carried out for a very high-profile client. Without Tony Hunt's vision, however, and his skilfully written performance specification for the structure, the building would probably never have been built. This project therefore gives an indication of the contribution of Tony Hunt to the rise and success of the Foster practice. In succeeding years, Foster and Hunt would collaborate on a number of other flat-roofed and steel-framed buildings. The IBM building at Cosham, however, and its predecessor the Newport School project, were perhaps the most crucial because it was with these that the working methodology became established.

Photo: Anthony Hunt Associates

Fig. 4.7. IBM Pilot Head Office, Cosham, England. Construction shot showing the Metsec steel framework which was erected using no item of plant larger than a fork-lift truck.

Fig. 4.8. Modern Art Glass Office and Warehouse, Thamesmead, London, England. Foster Associates, 1973.

Single-volume sheds

During the 1970s, Foster Associates designed three buildings which, though they had much in common with the single-envelope enclosures considered above, were distinctively different from them. These were an office and warehouse for Modern Art Glass (MAG) at Thamesmead in London, a school for children with special needs (Palmerston Special School) in Liverpool and the Sainsbury Centre for the Visual Arts in Norwich. The characteristics which they shared were a low-pitch roof, wrap-around cladding covering the roof and side walls, with no discontinuity at the eaves, and a fully glazed end wall. The final building of the trio — the Sainsbury Centre — was one of the most important works of British architecture of the second half of the twentieth century. Tony Hunt was the structural engineering consultant for all three.

The brief for the first of these buildings, the MAG warehouse and office (*Fig. 4.8*), specified a low-cost warehouse with attached office and showroom accommodation. As was now becoming something of a standard pattern, Foster chose to locate all of this within a single envelope of very simple overall form. On this occasion, however, the format adopted was that of a low-pitch portal-frame shed — potentially one of the most banal building forms imaginable. Tony Hunt's recollection was that it was chosen because it was the most economical form for the scale of building required.[66] As with previous projects, Foster and Hunt demonstrated that it was possible to make a work of architecture from a building type that accountants and developers had turned into the commonplace modern vernacular found on industrial estates throughout the world.

The general arrangement of the MAG building was an eight-bay portal frame shed (*Fig. 4.9*). Seven of these bays were occupied by the warehouse. The eighth consisted of a showroom at ground level with the office on a mezzanine floor above. This accommodation was separated from the warehouse by an internal wall zone which incorporated lavatories, store rooms and utilities and which also served as a fire break.

The structure of the MAG building consisted of nine 25 m span, I-section portal frameworks, spaced 7 m apart and carrying channel-section purlins and side rails to which the cladding was attached. It was self-bracing in the plane of the main frameworks, and diagonal bracing in the wall and roof planes in two of the eight bays provided stability in the along-building direction. The foundation consisted of a reinforced raft on multiple, short-bored piles. The arrangement was conventional –'one of the easiest buildings that we have done'[67] — and the calculations and detailed designs were carried out personally by Hunt.

Two features, in particular, distinguish the building from its run-of-the-mill contemporaries. One was the wrap-around cladding, the key feature of which was the smooth, minimum-radius curved transition between the roof and wall cladding. This allowed the elimination of gutters and downpipes — the rainwater simply flowed down the sides of the building to be collected by a ground level drain. The other striking features of the building were the all-glass end wall, that signalled the location of the office and showroom, and the refinement of the junction between this end wall and the wall and roof cladding (*Fig. 4.10*).

Both Foster and Hunt had by this time become very interested in cladding, particularly the glazing of buildings, and the design of the cladding for this building, both the glass wall and the profiled metal, represented a significant departure from previous practice. In Tony Hunt's words, 'this was the technology bit coming in'.[68] The profiled metal cladding was a standard system but the small-radius curved junction between the wall and roof was not, and it was difficult to find a manufacturer who could produce the non-standard eaves panels. This detail also required that the knee joints in the portal frames be of a non-standard pattern, which, in turn, required that a bespoke structure be designed in house by Tony Hunt. The glass end wall was specially designed for the building by Foster Associates, in collaboration with Martin Francis.

This building was significant because it marked the end of the use of 'found' components and the start of a method of working in which the design team would collaborate closely with component suppliers to produce systems of cladding and structure that were unique to the buildings in which they were installed. It is interesting to note that this approach was fundamental to the success of the SCSD system by Ehrenkrantz.

The Palmerston Special School (*Fig. 4.11*) was jointly commissioned by the Liverpool Education Department and the Spastics Society to provide facilities for the education of 60 handicapped children between the ages of 14 and 16. It was designed to conform to ideas on the therapeutic effect of surroundings on mentally handicapped children that envisaged the manipulation of space, light, colour, pattern and textures to produce interiors that were both stimulating and calming. Flexibility in the use of teaching spaces was also called for.

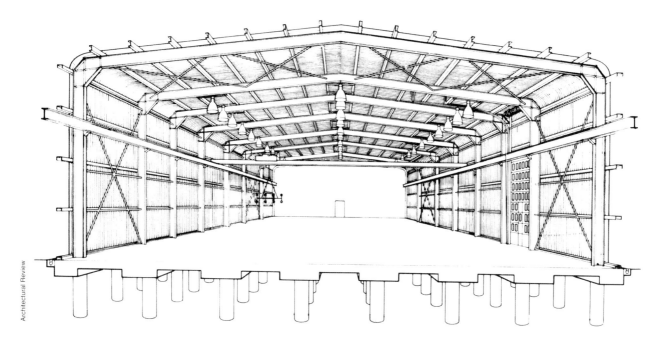

Foster's response to the brief was a deep-plan building similar to the flat-roofed single-envelope enclosures, such as the IBM Pilot Head Office. At Palmerston School, however, a five-bay pitched roof was employed, to give a domestic scale, with wrap-around cladding and an all-glass end wall — using a similar vocabulary to that of the MAG building. The design was informed by the experience that Foster Associates had had with a previous school for handicapped children that they had built in Hackney, London, in 1970–72, and by meticulous research into current thinking on the education of handicapped children.

The plan (Fig. 4.12) was based on a spine which occupied the central bay and in which were located the entrance, dining and common

Fig. 4.9. Modern Art Glass Office and Warehouse, Thamesmead, London, England. Perspective showing the structural arrangement of the Modern Art Glass Warehouse.

Fig. 4.10. Modern Art Glass Office and Warehouse, Thamesmead, London, England. The quality of the detailing of this building distinguishes it from the majority of portal frame sheds.

Photo: Foster Associates

Fig. 4.11. Palmerston School, Liverpool, England.

made the frame stable in all directions and eliminated the need for diagonal bracing in the wall or roof planes. The building was clad in yellow-coloured asbestos cement sheeting, for reasons of economy, and the slightly clumsy appearance that inevitably occurs with this material contrasts with the extreme elegance of the structural framework.

Much effort was expended in refining the appearance of this structure and, in discussing this with the author, Tony Hunt reflected on the question of structural elegance:

'There has never been any sense of throwing a structure together', but rather the taking of 'immense care at every stage — concept, analysis, manufacture'.[69]

Thus, the immense care that the architects devoted to the formulation of the brief, the planning of the interior and the detailing of the fabric was matched by that taken by the structural engineers to produce a visually satisfying structure.

The Palmerston School building won the International Prize for Architecture in 1976 and received an RIBA Award Commendation in 1977. The building was not successful in the long term, however, mainly due to changes in the political climate that surrounded education in the 1980s. It was demolished in 1989.

The portal-frame shed form, with wrap-around cladding and glass end walls, pioneered by Foster in the MAG and Palmerston School buildings was to find its greatest architectural

activity areas. Four service cores, with lavatories and other utilities, subdivided the main teaching area into four open-plan sections. The glass end wall was recessed from the edge of the cladding to provide a covered, outdoor activity area.

As with previous Foster buildings, the structure and cladding were kept simple and economical and the money thus saved was used to improve the quality of the interior. The five-bay portal framework, in square hollow-section steelwork, was one of the most refined ever produced by Tony Hunt. The inherent efficiency of the pitched roof form, the shortness of the spans and the structural continuity that resulted from the all-welded construction and rigid column-to-slab junctions allowed very slender elements to be used. The rigid column bases also expression in the much larger Sainsbury Centre for the Visual Arts at the University of East Anglia in Norwich, England (*Fig. 4.13*). The Sainsbury Centre was, however, much more than simply the culmination of a series of designs based on the idea of the portal frame shed. With this building, Foster took forward ideas that had been developing over a decade and synthesised them into the Modern shed equivalent of the cathedral.

The Sainsbury Centre project grew out of the desire of Sir Robert and Lady Sainsbury to gift their extensive collection of visual art to the nation. This gift was not to be made to a national museum or gallery, however, but to a university

'... *because we want to give some men and women — and who better than undergraduates in a School of Fine Arts — the opportunity of looking at works of art in the natural context of their work and daily life, not just because they have been prompted to visit a museum or art gallery ....*'[70]

The Sainsburys also funded the construction of a new building to house the collection and the University Grants Council contributed to an associated building for the School of Fine Arts at the University of East Anglia. Other accommodation added as the brief developed included a senior common room, a restaurant for university and public use and a special exhibition area. Initially, it was assumed that these various functions would be accommodated in four separate buildings.

Several ideas informed the design, including the desire of the Sainsburys to avoid

the 'mausoleum type of art gallery'; the importance of flexibility for change in use and for growth; a desire to integrate social aspects of the design; the need for good security; and the need to service the main interior spaces without disturbing the activities going on within them by facilitating the changing and adjustment of lights and other forms of environmental control.

The evolution of the design is described in volume 2 of the Lambot series, which gives a glimpse of the often laborious iterative process by

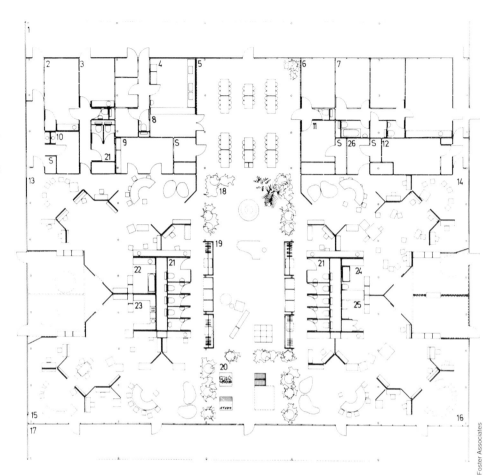

Foster Associates

Fig. 4.12. Palmerston School, Liverpool, England. Plan.

which the forms of such buildings are determined. The great simplicity and clarity of the form that finally emerged may seem in retrospect to be obvious, even inevitable but, as is often the case, it was the product of a great deal of design effort. In the final version all of the accommodation was located within a single building envelope of dramatically simple form. The finished building was a very large single-storey tube subdivided internally by two areas of mezzanine. The main public areas — the gallery and restaurant — were located on the ground floor adjacent to the walls at each end, and were separated by the university areas — the common room and the study and teaching rooms — located on and between the mezzanines. The external envelope consisted of two skins separated by a 2·4 m wide void that was used to accommodate services and utilities. Services were also placed in a spine, at basement level, which ran the entire length of the building.

Although, in the preliminary stages of the project, it was envisaged that the Centre would consist of a group of buildings, the concept of a single-volume envelope to house all of the main activities in a linear arrangement emerged fairly quickly. In the initial versions of this, the building had a single skin supported on a solid-web portal framework structure (*Fig. 4.14*). Various possibilities were investigated, some with the structure outside the skin and some with the structure inside the skin. In all of these, the structure was exposed and therefore formed a

Fig. 4.13. Sainsbury Centre for the Visual Arts, Norwich, England.

prominent part of the visual vocabulary. The 'industrial' character of the large I-section girders was eventually felt by Foster to be inappropriate for a building devoted to the visual arts and a decision was taken, on aesthetic grounds, to change to a triangulated form of structure that would be lighter in appearance and more neutral in its visual language.[71] This turned out to be one of the most crucial decisions in the whole design because it opened up the possibility of using a voided, double-membrane external skin to create a combined structure and services zone around the entire perimeter of the building's cross-section.

Following the rejection of the solid-web structure by Foster, the possibility of using an aluminium Triodetic space frame was investigated in detail. This would need to have been manufactured in Canada, where the makers of Triodetic were based, and time constraints caused it to be abandoned and forced the adoption of a purpose-designed structure in steel, which was fabricated by Tubeworkers Ltd.

In its final form, the building had a wrap-around skin that, like its predecessors at MAG and Palmerston School, was identical on the walls and roof. In this case, however, it consisted of outer and inner membranes separated by a 2·4 m wide structural zone. In the walls, this zone was used to accommodate services and small-volume spaces such as lavatories and darkrooms (*Fig. 4.15*). In the corresponding roof zone, access walkways allowed the main spaces to be serviced without disruption of their activities. This idea, to locate plant and small-scale spaces in a very thick, voided outer skin and thereby release the main space to fulfil its primary function unencumbered by these intrusions, was a major breakthrough in the design of the building. It allowed great clarity and simplicity to be achieved in the placing of functions within the main space (*Fig. 4.16*).

The cladding system was one of the most distinctive features and was a significant progression from those employed at MAG and Palmerston School. It represented a further step, for Foster, away from the use of off-the-peg products of industry in the direction of components that were specially crafted for specific buildings. The system used at the Sainsbury Centre was developed specially for the

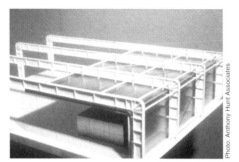

Photo: Anthony Hunt Associates

Fig. 4.14. Sainsbury Centre for the Visual Arts, Norwich, England. Model of early scheme with solid web I-section exoskeletal structure and single-skin cladding.

building by Foster Associates, in association with British Aluminium, Modern Art Glass and with Tony Pritchard acting as cladding consultant.

The driving idea was the now familiar one of flexibility. The intention was to produce detachable cladding which would consist of a series of small panels that could be easily interchanged to meet the varying requirements of the interior (*Fig. 4.17*). The panels measured 1800 mm by 1200 mm and were of two basic types (solid and transparent) with special curved versions to accommodate the wall-to-roof junction. The solid panels were a sandwich of two skins of highly malleable aluminium alloy separated by a 100 mm thick phenolic foam core. The transparent panels had the same moulded aluminium edge detail as the solid panels and also had an aluminium sub-frame to provide the necessary rigidity. Both types of panel were bolted directly to landing plates on the main structural elements. A neoprene gasket, in the form of a net

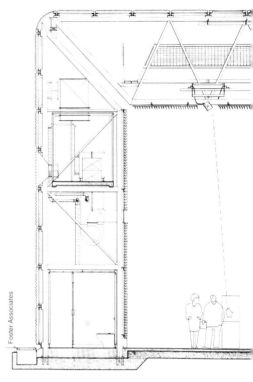

Foster Associates

Fig. 4.15. Sainsbury Centre for the Visual Arts, Norwich, England. Section through wall showing triangulated structure creating the 'thick' skin in which services, cloakrooms and other small scale spaces are located.

Fig. 4.16. Sainsbury Centre for the Visual Arts, Norwich, England. interior uncluttered by cloakrooms, etc. which are located in the thick walls.

which covered the entire building, provided a weathertight seal and gutter between the panels. The panels could easily be unbolted to allow the juxtaposition of solidity and transparency to be changed and this also allowed easy external access to the wall and roof spaces for maintenance and repair of services. The support requirements of this unique cladding system had a significant effect on the design of the structure.

The design of the structure evolved in parallel with the planning and general arrangement of the interior by the now customary process of dialogue among the various members of the design team. In the final version it consisted of a series of main frames, each of which was a simple post-and-beam form with a single horizontal element supported on two column elements (*Fig. 4.18*). These principal elements were configured identically as fully-triangulated space trusses of triangular cross-section with twin outer booms and a single inner boom. The junctions between them were of the hinge type with the load being transferred in a single joint at the top of the column element. Stability was provided by rigid column bases and there was no secondary structure. The support system for the building consisted of 37 of these three-part frameworks set alongside each other (*Fig. 4.18*).

The structure was self-bracing in the across-building direction but wind girders were provided for stability in the along-building direction and were formed by triangulating the planes between the inner booms of the horizontal and vertical elements of selected adjacent main frames. Wind girders were provided at each end of the building, to receive the wind loading from the glass end walls which spanned vertically from the floor slab to the lower booms of the main frames, and also adjacent to two expansion joints along its length. Where these girders occurred, an extra connection was required between the horizontal and vertical elements of the main frames, at the inner side of the corners, and these connections are visible in the end elevations of the building.

The structure of the Sainsbury Centre is unusual and innovatory in several respects resulting from the need to preserve the integrity of

Fig. 4.17. Sainsbury Centre for the Visual Arts, Norwich, England. Cladding panels are mounted directly on the primary structure and are demountable for access and maintenance.

the strong architectural concept of the tube-like single-volume building with the wrap-around double-membrane skin. The building is a good illustration of the nature of the relationship between architecture and engineering in this kind of late Modern architecture.

Tony Hunt's task in the development of the design of the Sainsbury Centre was to produce a structure which was light and efficient in appearance, of constant and equal depth in the roof and wall zones and which supported the delicate membrane of the building with apparently effortless ease. The main problem was that a very strong and rigid structure was

required, despite the fact that the loads to be carried were relatively light.

The shape of the building's cross-section, to which the structure obviously had to conform, was not ideal from a structural point of view. The overall form of a structure affects the pattern and intensity of the internal forces that occur within it and the most efficient forms are those that result in the lowest levels of internal force, especially bending-type internal force, for a given application of load. The cross-sectional form of the Sainsbury Centre was such that fairly high levels of bending moment resulted from relatively small amounts of load.[72]

The shape of the building's cross-section was also such that a significant variation in the intensity of internal forces occurred across the span. In purely engineering structures, such as bridges, this can be accommodated by varying the depth of the structure — making it deeper where greater bending strength is required — and also by varying the weights of the sub-elements in conformity with the varying patterns of internal force. Such a solution was not available at the Sainsbury Centre because it would have conflicted with the requirement, dictated by the aesthetics of the cross-section, for a structure that was of uniform appearance around the entire perimeter of the building's cross-section. The architectural concept of a structural zone of uniform thickness and appearance, wrapping around the enclosed spaces and visible in the end elevation, conflicted with the reality of the structural function.

Fig. 4.18. Sainsbury Centre for the Visual Arts, Norwich, England. Construction shot showing triangulated girders arranged in a simple post-and-beam format with no secondary structure.

Photo: Anthony Hunt Associates

Fig. 4.19. Sainsbury Centre for the Visual Arts, Norwich, England. Construction shot showing cladding being attached directly to the primary elements. The wind girder, formed by inserting cross bracing between the inner booms of adjacent frames, is also visible. This required that the main elements be linked at the inner as well as the outer side of the knee joint. This feature occurred only at the ends of the building and at two internal expansion joints.

The relatively long span of 35 m exacerbated the problem. Where spans are short, the need for varying strength along the length of a structure can be easily masked if a structure of uniform appearance is required for aesthetic purposes. This was done at Palmerston School where an elegant portal frame was achieved in square hollow-sections of constant depth. The depth adopted was dictated by the magnitude of the highest level of internal force, which occurred at the building's eaves. At all other locations, the structure was stronger than was strictly necessary but the relatively small magnitudes of the maximum internal forces allowed a small structural depth to be specified and the parallel-sided elements were therefore light and graceful in appearance. At MAG, where the span was intermediate between those at the Palmerston School and the Sainsbury Centre, the structure had to be deepened at the eaves joint but this did not detract from its appearance.

The much larger span at the Sainsbury Centre made it difficult to achieve the uniformity of structural depth that was used at the Palmerston School but, for visual reasons, it was essential that this be accomplished. Two features of the design solved the problem.

The first of these was the depth of the structure which had a relatively low ratio of span to depth of 13·76. This atypically large depth was primarily a consequence of the requirement to produce wall and roof zones that were of sufficient volume to accommodate services and utilities and was not determined from purely structural considerations. It resulted in small internal forces in the longitudinal elements of the main girders, however, and allowed very slender sub-elements to be specified. It is interesting to observe here that the satisfaction of more than one design requirement, by the selection of a particular feature, in this case the thick wall leading to the large structural depth, is frequently a characteristic of a well-resolved building.

The second device that was adopted to cope with the less than ideal structural profile was the manipulation of the distribution of internal forces by the judicious placing of hinge joints (*Fig. 4.20*) in the main frames. At the Sainsbury Centre, the internal forces at the eaves joints would have been excessively high if the structure had been continuous at these points, as is normal with portal frames. By connecting the horizontal and vertical elements with hinge-type joints, the internal forces at the corners were minimized, thus eliminating the need to increase the depth of the structure at these points. The idea of arranging the locations of the hinges in a structure in order to achieve the most favourable distribution of internal forces is a well-known, standard device of structural engineering, but a highly unusual and innovatory use was made of it here.

Another uncommon feature of the Sainsbury Centre structure was that it did not conform to the conventional primary/secondary structural arrangement, in which a limited number of main frames, spaced at around 6 m to 10 m centres, span across a building, with a secondary structure of purlins and cladding rails bridging the gap between them. This standard arrangement is considered sensible because it limits the number of elements which must be sufficiently strong and heavy to span across the entire width of the building. With this arrangement a secondary structure is required because the cladding is rarely capable of supporting itself across the gap between the main elements, but the primary/secondary arrangement normally results, nevertheless, in a structure that is lighter than one in which all elements span across the building.

This standard arrangement could not be used at the Sainsbury Centre because the secondary structure would not have provided sufficient rigidity to meet the demanding requirements of the cladding system in respect of deflection under varying load. The massive primary trusses, which had the required rigidity, were therefore simply stacked alongside one another, and the cladding attached directly to them (*Fig. 4.19*). This 'bunching' of the primary structural elements resulted in a much heavier structure than would otherwise have been required to provide an enclosure of the size of the Sainsbury Centre. Tony Hunt frankly admits that it was not the most efficient structure that could have been provided but maintains that its use was justified in the service of preserving the architectural idea. As Tony Hunt observed, it was curiously appropriate:

'There was an expectation that the building would be extended, following its completion, and it did seem appropriate that this tube-like linear form should have been built up in slices.'[73]

He also points out that:

'This structural arrangement of linked primaries provided an incredibly efficient platform for a totally repetitive cladding system. Thus, [it is] not an 'optimum structure' but an economic, efficient total enclosure.'[74]

To summarise the structural achievement in the Sainsbury Centre, the structure that Tony Hunt's design team finally evolved satisfied the architectural requirements remarkably well and produced a happy compatibility of structural and aesthetic functions. It provided the necessary support for the demanding cladding system. It

Fig. 4.20. Sainsbury Centre for the Visual Arts, Norwich, England. Detail of hinge connection between the main elements.

Photo: Anthony Hunt Associates

Fig. 4.21. Sainsbury Centre for the Visual Arts, Norwich, England.

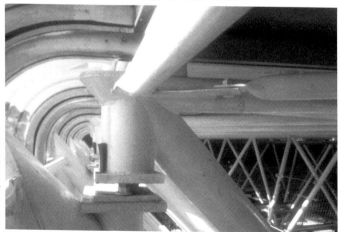

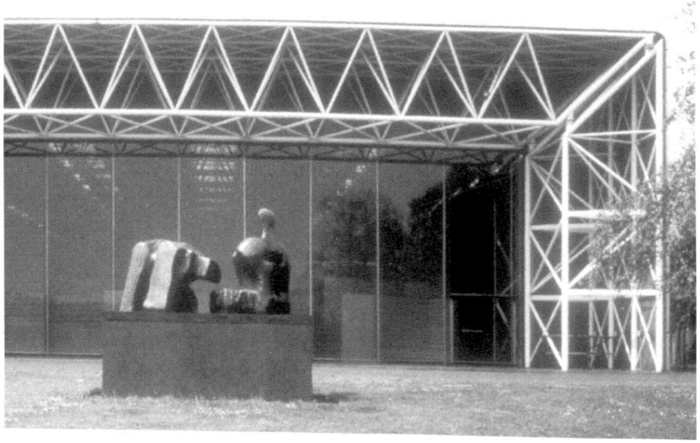

Photo: Anthony Hunt Associates

allowed the required services and utilities void within the building's outer skin and did not obstruct it with high-volume structural elements. It was itself a thing of elegance, with slender sub-elements and carefully-detailed connections, which enhanced the appearance of the building.

That this was achieved in the face of the very challenging problems of structural design says much for the quality of the engineering design. When the overall form and general arrangement of a structure are less than ideal, from a structural point of view, and produce high concentrations of internal force, the structure can all too easily become an ungainly affair of badly-proportioned and crudely-connected sub-elements. Such a solution would never have been acceptable to Hunt. The challenge of the Sainsbury Centre (Fig. 4.21) was to produce an elegant structure from seriously difficult constraints and boundary conditions. This was finally achieved through a combination of knowledge, creative thinking, dialogue and a great deal of painstaking work in the refinement of the design by all members of the team.

Willis, Faber and Dumas building, Ipswich

The Willis, Faber and Dumas (WFD) building (Fig. 4.22) is a four-storey office for a large multi-national insurance company. It is situated in Ipswich, England, and was commissioned because the client wished to locate a major part of its operation outside, but in reasonable proximity to, London. Ipswich was chosen for its pleasant

Photo. Anthony Hunt Associates

townscape, good facilities and good communications links.

The building was a remarkable creation:

'... as close to the real-life proclamation of the crystalline dreams of Taut and the early Mies as we are likely to get — an all-glass architecture.'[75]

'... a benchmark in post-war modernism.'[76]

That an interesting new building, by a rising young architectural practice, should receive favourable treatment in the architectural press is not surprising. What is more remarkable about the WFD building is that it should also have been greatly appreciated and praised by its owners and users.

'... a splendid place in which to work, and one especially suitable for Willis Faber.'[77]

The WFD building is a rare example of a late twentieth-century building that satisfies all the architectural requirements: it works in every respect — visually, socially, as townscape, as a workplace and as an object of quality that people are pleased to be associated with and to care for. It was the product of the happy combination of a talented and dedicated design team and an

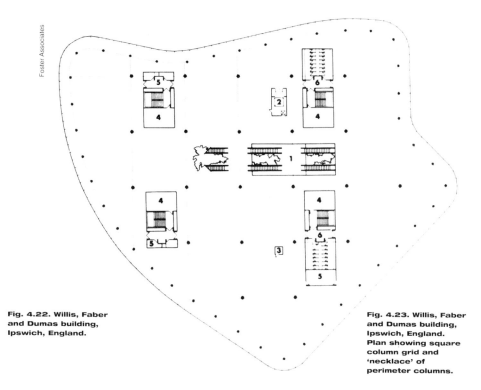

Fig. 4.22. Willis, Faber and Dumas building, Ipswich, England.

Fig. 4.23. Willis, Faber and Dumas building, Ipswich, England. Plan showing square column grid and 'necklace' of perimeter columns.

Fig. 4.24. Willis, Faber and Dumas building, Ipswich, England. Reflective, currilinear glass exterior wall.

enlightened client, who was not only sympathetic to the architectural issues but who also recognised and respected their importance.

As with the other buildings that have been described in this chapter, the final scheme for the WFD building is so appropriate as to seem obvious. It was, however, the product of the lengthy iterative design process that was by this time customary between Foster and Hunt. The evolution of the design has been well documented[78] and is described here only in outline.

The story begins with the clients, Willis, Faber and Dumas, who were cautious about the selection of the architect. They had already secured the site, in the architecturally sensitive market town of Ipswich, and were conscious of the need to get the building right. As befitted an insurance company, they wished to have a distinguished building but the Board of WFD also expressed a desire for 'nothing over-ambitious yet on the other hand not too pedestrian'.[79] They consulted the RIBA about possible designers and were helped to prepare a shortlist of 'distinguished' architects. Foster was ultimately selected for his track record of professionalism in delivering stylish buildings on time, to tight schedules and within budget.

At the time of Foster's appointment the brief was still evolving. Initially, it called for two buildings, one for WFD's own use and one for letting purposes. During the early stages of the design WFD continued to increase the size of the site by acquiring extra pockets of land and it was in the end fairly large in relation to the floor area required. It was also of irregular shape, bounded by a curving pattern of streets and lanes of medieval origin.

Many possible schemes were investigated by the Foster team, including some with moderately high tower-type buildings, but the final solution abandoned the idea of having two buildings and proposed a single building occupying the whole of the available site. This allowed the required accommodation to be provided in a low-rise four-storey building and was more respectful of the existing townscape than towers would have been. It was a key aspect of the building's success and represented a break with the more normal Modernist solution for corporate offices in which a tall building is made to occupy a relatively small part of a site, the remainder of which is hard-landscaped to provide open space at ground level. Open space was not particularly required in a small market town in rural England and the avoidance of a dominating and potentially oppressive tall building was considered to be a

more important consideration. The decision to extend the footprint of the building over the whole of the irregular form of the site was a demonstration of the continual questioning of accepted practice and standard solutions that was central to Foster's methodology. The search for appropriateness was allowed to take the design in whatever direction was necessary to make a sensible response to the particular circumstances. In this case it involved the abandonment of rectilinearity. The adoption of a low-rise solution also led to the dropping of the idea of incorporating lettable space into the project.

The client's concern for the wellbeing of its employees had an important influence on the brief. Much of the daily activity of the workforce was of a routine and mundane nature and WFD were anxious that the working environment should be humane and conducive to the creation of a pleasurable and healthy work experience. This requirement fell easily on the ears of Foster for whom the creation of a working environment that was sympathetic to human values had always been given a high priority. It affected virtually all aspects of the design. Of particular significance were the incorporation into the brief of a restaurant and cafeteria, with associated kitchens, and the provision of amenities such as a swimming pool and roof garden. The planning of the circulation routes within the building was also greatly influenced by a concern for the quality of the experience that would be provided as people moved around within it.

In the final design the building was a four-storey office of irregular, curvilinear and very deep plan (*Fig. 4.23*). Open-plan office accommodation was provided on the first and second floors and was served by four cores containing lavatories, lifts and ducting. The ground floor acted as the reception area and also housed the swimming pool and plant rooms. The principal means of access between floors was by a central atrium containing escalators. This also admitted top light into the centre of the deep plan. On the office floors circulation was at the perimeter in a 3 m wide zone adjacent to the external wall. At roof level, the restaurant, cafeteria and kitchens were located in a glass-walled cupola of rectangular plan which was centred on the escalator well. This capping building occupied around half of the plan area of the roof and the remainder was laid in turf to serve as a roof garden.

One of the most remarkable features of the building is the faceted all-glass curtain wall (*Fig. 4.24*). This was developed by Foster Associates with Martin Francis and Pilkington Brothers Ltd. Two schemes were investigated, one with the glass supported on tubular steel mullions fixed to the floor slabs and one with the complete wall suspended from the edge of the roof slab and given lateral support only by the lower floors. The second scheme was adopted. The wall was subdivided into vertical modules each consisting of six glass plates in a vertical line, hung from the edge of the roof slab and connected together by

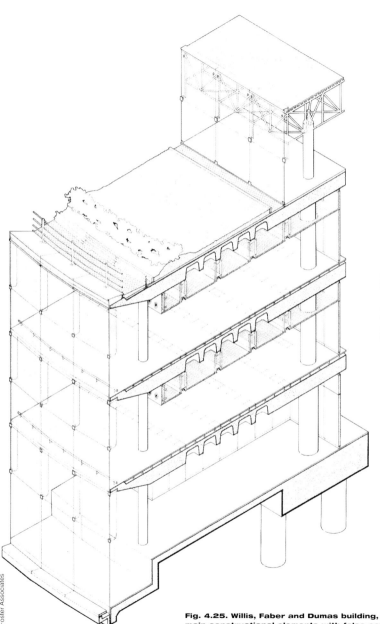

Foster Associates

Photo: Foster and Partners

Fig. 4.26. Willis, Faber and Dumas building, Ipswich, England. Roof garden.

Fig. 4.25. Willis, Faber and Dumas building, Ipswich, England. Axonometric showing arrangement of main constructional elements with false ceilings creating service zones below each floor slab.

patch fittings. The joints between the glass were filled with silicon sealant which, if a panel broke, was sufficiently strong to allow panels deprived of support from above to be supported by adjacent panels. Lateral support for the wall was provided by glass fins, of half-storey height, bolted to the undersides of the edges of the floor slabs. The connections between the fins and the glass wall allowed vertical movement to occur, to accommodate thermal expansion and variations in the deflections of adjacent floors caused by differential loading and creep.

The structure of the WFD building is a 700 mm deep, two-way spanning in situ reinforced-concrete coffered slab[80] supported on a 14 m square grid of circular cross-section columns (1 m diameter from ground to first floor; 800 mm diameter from first to third floor) (Fig. 4.25). A ring of columns at 7 m centres and of 600 mm diameter, sometimes referred to as the 'necklace', was placed around the perimeter to support areas of floor which are not located within the main column grid. The floor slab cantilevers 3 m beyond these and tapers to an edge of 250 mm thickness. Lateral stability is provided by rigid-frame action between the floor slabs and the principal columns. Deep piled (30 m long) foundations with in situ reinforced-concrete pile caps were used due to problems with swallow-holes in the chalk substratum, and the ground floor slab and swimming pool are fully suspended between pile caps, the side walls of the pool acting as deep beams.

The structure of the WFD building is almost a textbook demonstration of the advantages of one of the most standard ways of making a multi-storey building in reinforced concrete. The two-way spanning, beam-less coffered slab is perhaps the most efficient and cost-effective way of providing the structural armature for a multi-storey building, combining a relatively high degree of structural efficiency with great simplicity of construction.[81] These virtues were fully exploited at WFD.

The 14 m column grid at WFD gave the best compromise between the need for planning freedom within floors and control of the structural depth and therefore of overall storey height. The fact that the structural depth was small, with no downstand beams, had the further advantage of making possible an unobstructed zone under the slab for distribution of services. The high degree of structural continuity which is present and the mouldability of reinforced concrete allowed the irregular plan form to be made without difficulty and the floor to be easily cantilevered beyond the perimeter columns and tapered to a fine edge. The structural continuity facilitated the transition from the regular column grid of the interior to the curvilinear support pattern of the necklace of perimeter columns. It also allowed the omission of large areas of floor to create the atrium. The structure is therefore a standard system, exploited to the full in the creation of a highly innovative building.

Architecturally, the building is an example of Modernism at its best, in which structural and architectural design are perfectly combined. It presents an object lesson in how to place a large commercial building into the small-scale urban fabric of a market town. The overall height of the building was in scale with the surroundings and was kept small by the occupation of the whole of the available site. The highly efficient structural system contributed to the low overall height by allowing storey heights to be small. The preservation of the original street pattern, by accepting the irregularity of the site, was also important. Again, the structural system allowed this to be accommodated without difficulty. Finally, the cladding of the building in tinted glass generated interesting reflections of the existing townscape and the building as a result makes a positive contribution to the urban landscape.

The building was also remarkable for the care that was taken to provide a humane working environment. The provision of amenities such as the restaurant, cafeteria, roof garden and swimming pool (Figs 4.26 and 4.27) were all important aspects of this. The central atrium was another (Fig. 4.28). This helped to create a central focus and admitted sunlight into the deep plan. It opened up greater possibilities for social interaction, as people moved around the building, than would have been possible with the lifts and narrow enclosed stairs that are more normal in office buildings. The idea of the perimeter zone, for circulation within floors (Fig. 4.29), created similar psychological benefits and made routes

Photo: Anthony Hunt Associates

Fig. 4.27. Willis, Faber and Dumas building, Ipswich, England. Swimming pool.

Photo: Anthony Hunt Associates

Fig. 4.29. Willis, Faber and Dumas building, Ipswich, England. Perimeter circulation route.

that were superior to the windowless corridors that are found in most multi-storey buildings. The incorporation of these features was dependent on a compatible structural arrangement.

Both structurally and architecturally the building is a fairly straight piece of Modern architecture, on the one hand, and highly innovatory, on the other. It could be regarded as a straightforward realisation of Le Corbusier's famous 'five points' of 1922. It represents the disconnection of structure from the functions of enclosing and subdividing space that Le Corbusier identified as the architectural significance of the structural framework. It also incorporates the idea of returning the footprint of a building to nature in the form of a roof garden. It exploits the potential of these concepts, however, in a way that was never achieved by Le Corbusier himself.

Conclusion

The buildings that have been described in this chapter were the ones which established the reputation of the Foster practice in the 1970s and which formed the basis from which he launched an international career in the 1980s. Tony Hunt made a very significant personal contribution to all of them and was therefore an important factor in both the rise of Foster to a position of prominence in his profession and in determining the direction taken by this type of British architecture.

Fig. 4.28. Willis, Faber and Dumas building, Ipswich, England. Escalator well which forms the principal route for vertical circulation.

Photo: Foster and Partners

Chapter Five
Hunt and Rogers

Chapter Five
Hunt and Rogers

Introduction

Richard Rogers, in the collaboration with Norman Foster and Tony Hunt that produced the Reliance Controls building, may be regarded as a joint founder of the British architectural movement that became known as High Tech. Despite the closeness of their association, however, Rogers and Foster went on to develop architecturally along quite different lines.

Foster's subsequent architecture can be seen to have developed naturally from the ideas that came together at Reliance Controls. It was largely a matter of making buildings that were pristine objects — exquisitely detailed assemblages of metal and glass based on simple, diagrammatic plans — in a tradition whose most outstanding previous exponent in terms of philosophy had been Ludwig Mies van der Rohe. This type of architecture derives ultimately from classicism. It has its roots in Antiquity where the first of the pristine objects in the western architectural tradition — the Greek temples — were created and its most crucial aspect is an idea of beauty that was articulated by Alberti at the time of the Italian Renaissance:

'Beauty is that reasoned harmony of all the parts within a body, so that nothing may be added, taken away, or altered, but for the worse.[82]

To achieve this kind of beauty the designer must seek after perfection.[83]

A characteristic of form that aspires to perfection is that, as Alberti stated, it has a fundamental quality of 'unalterableness'. Foster's buildings have the adamantine quality of apparent completeness that is associated with the search for visual perfection. The Sainsbury Centre may serve as an example. When Foster was commissioned to extend this building he chose to place the extension underground so that the form and setting of the original would not be affected. This was despite the fact that the tube-like form of the original was developed partly to allow for likely subsequent extension. The final version of the first building proved to be too powerful, however, to admit of disruption or adaptation even by its creator. Control, and its expression in built form, is an important aspect of this type of architecture; Foster's skill (organisational, technical, visual) is used to control every aspect of the final outcome, which clearly conveys the idea that nothing has been left to chance.

Rogers' approach to design was and remains more pragmatic:

'Our architecture is more additive — more unfinished. The concept is that a building should be able to be added to rather than finite. We see buildings more like pieces of modern poetry — additive.[84]

In Rogers' work there is no sense of obligation to 'dress up' the untidiness of the world in a vision of perfection that he would regard as spurious. An early instance of this difference of approach between Foster and Rogers occurred at Reliance Controls and concerned the recessing of the light fittings within the corrugations of the roof decking (*Fig. 3.9*). This was a visually pleasing solution but was impractical because it made the fittings more difficult to maintain and replace. Foster had no difficulty accepting this. Rogers would have preferred an alternative, more practical solution.[85]

In the architecture that Rogers developed independently of Foster the intention was that a building should first and foremost be a useful object, in a practical sense, and be assembled in a logical way. From the late twentieth century onwards, flexibility has been an important aspect of usefulness and may operate to different timescales for different parts of a building because the different elements — structure, services, cladding and partitioning — wear out or become obsolete at different rates. In Rogers' buildings these elements are separate and discrete systems so that they can be modified or replaced to different timescales. They are also highly accessible and not concealed or tidied away behind false ceilings or elaborate cladding systems. Ironically, this articulation of the elements of a building can render it less useful to its users as opposed to those who build or maintain it and this is a criticism that has been made of many of Rogers' buildings, most notably the Centre Pompidou in Paris and the Lloyd's Headquarters building in London.

The separation and accessibility of systems facilitates another of Rogers' ideas, namely that the building should honestly express its functions. Structure should look like structure, cladding like cladding and services like services. The building should, in other words, be 'readable'. The reality of the separation of systems is therefore expressed visually and this makes the architecture.

Rogers is not so much concerned with making buildings of refined appearance as with expressing the functions of their various parts. Buildings are rather, for him, dynamic things, subject to and capable of continuous change in response to the changing needs of their users and of society. The visual qualities are, nevertheless, extremely important for Rogers and the combination of the expression of function and its physical reality is the constant challenge of his kind of architecture.

Rogers may be considered as operating in the Gothic rather than the Classical tradition. Just as the built forms of monasteries and feudal houses of medieval Europe grew and were expanded to cope with the changing needs and functions of their users and frequently acquired irregular and often apparently random forms, so the buildings that Rogers designs are intended to have forms derived from changing twentieth-century functions. The pioneers in Britain of the attempt to develop this approach in a Modernist context were Alison and Peter Smithson and the self-styled visionaries of the Archigram group — who had a significant influence on Rogers. His experiences in the USA were also important. Design by teamwork with the technical professions, the method favoured by Rogers as

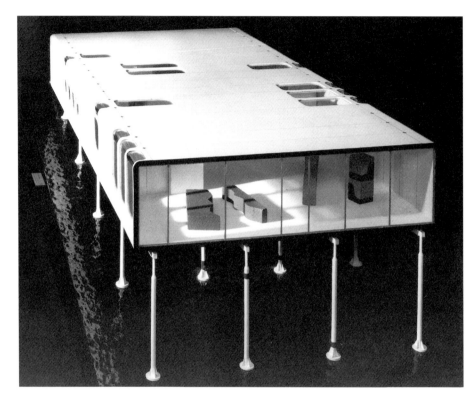

Fig. 5.1. Zip-up enclosure.

well as Foster, was necessary for its success and it was here that Tony Hunt was important.

The work of Foster and of Rogers therefore developed along quite different lines: Foster became the urbane tailor of the immaculately-cut suit, Rogers the maker of practical designer clothing, and it is interesting to note that these ways of working were expressive of their respective backgrounds, personalities and upbringing. In Appleyard's biography, Rogers is portrayed as an adventurous young man, who travelled extensively in the post-war Europe of the 1940s and 50s. Though he was English by birth, his parents were cultured, middle-class Italians who had moved to Britain in the 1930s to escape from the Fascist regime. They retained contacts with Italy, however, and, according to Appleyard, these family ties with sections of the Italian intelligentsia stood the young and penniless Rogers in good stead in his travels.

Rogers seems not to have had a childhood ambition to become an architect. He came to architecture later in life than Foster and without the traditional skills of drafting technique and visual presentation that are so essential to the successful passage through a school of architecture. Rogers approached architecture with words — not the words of the intellectual, rather those of the discourser — and it was fortunate that his cousin Ernesto Rogers, a notable Italian architect and sometime editor of both *Casabella* and *Domus*, encouraged him to become a student at the Architectural Association (AA) in London, where emphasis was placed on concept and with the architect's contribution to the making of a better world, rather than with formalism, technique and awkward questions of visual detail.[86] It has been said[87] that the AA was probably the only architectural school in Britain at the time in which Rogers could have survived. All of the other schools were attempting to emulate the doctrinaire and quasi-religious system of the Bauhaus and it was only at the Architectural Association that free discourse could

have been accepted as an alternative to the traditional architectural virtues of the Modernist mainstream — formalist designs, drafting ability and technical control.

In 1967, following the break up of Team 4, Rogers and his first wife Su set up the firm of Richard and Su Rogers and took into partnership John Young, a former employee of Team 4. The first commissions were for private houses, for Humphrey Spender, at Utling in Essex, and for Rogers' parents at Wimbledon in London. These were executed in the design language of the Reliance Controls factory which featured steel frameworks supporting lightweight industrially-produced cladding. As with most young practices, commissions not generated by friends or relatives were slow to appear at first and Rogers and his associates had time to work on competition entries. The most significant of these was the design they produced for the 1968 House for Today competition which they called the 'Zip-up' enclosure (*Fig. 5.1*). This scheme was not built but it was important for clarifying the architectural ideas that would inform later work executed by Rogers and his team.

The paucity of commissions also provided Rogers with the opportunity to think and write about architecture and this resulted in two 'manifesti', written in 1969, which give an insight into his approach. The first of these consisted largely of an attack on the existing system of architectural education in Britain. Rogers accused the universities of being

'... *closed authoritarian institutions operated primarily for the benefit of those running the institutions ...*'[88]

and the piece ended with a more general attack on the professional establishment of architecture:

'*The way to justify the need for architects is not by creating a closed shop as propagated by the RIBA and most of the schools it controls, but by throwing the profession open to all those who are interested so that architecture becomes a truly multi-disciplinary activity. Only when all answers become the outcome of necessity, expediency and economy, will the architect and student be in a position to question whether an object is needed at all, and to suggest to the client a complete reconsideration of any problem.*'

This refreshing statement stemmed both from the natural impatience of youth with convention and from the feeling of impotence that besets young idealists who feel that they have the answers but that the world is not listening. It gives a hint of the rebellious and iconoclastic side of Rogers' nature and is also clearly the statement of an outsider who had found it difficult to accept or accommodate the conventions of the educational or professional establishments.[89] By the time this statement was made Rogers had accumulated a fair degree of architectural experience, so it was also a clear and worthy challenge to the formalist approach to architecture of the mainstream Modernists who dominated the scene.[90]

The reference to 'multi-disciplinary activity' is perhaps the most significant part of the quotation. Rogers, like Foster, believed that the design of a building should be a truly collaborative effort involving all relevant disciplines including architects, structural engineers, services engineers and quantity surveyors. This design-team method of working was crucial to the emergence of High Tech because the style depended on the development of systems of structure and services that were visually pleasing as well as functional. The best way of achieving this was to have architects and engineers actively collaborating on all stages of the design. Rogers' quest for a refreshed version of Modern architecture, in which exposed structure and services would form a major part of the visual vocabulary, was therefore dependent on the existence of individuals like Tony Hunt who could deliver structure that functioned well technically and who were also prepared to enter into dialogues with architects to produce engineering that satisfied visual requirements.

Rogers' second manifesto of 1969 was an articulation of his ideas on how the design of buildings should be approached. He advocated that they should be general-purpose rather than tailor-made, so that the same shell could cater for different requirements, and that they should be capable of being erected quickly and constructed from a minimum number of prefabricated standard components assembled with dry joints. He also argued for the use of structures with

Photo: Anthony Hunt Associates

Fig. 5.2. Spender House, Utling, England. Richard and Su Rogers.

maximum spans to minimise interior obstructions and to allow partitions to be easily demounted.

In 1970 Rogers took the Italian architect/engineer Renzo Piano into partnership and the firm became known as Piano and Rogers. By this time Mike Davies and Marco Goldschmied had also joined and would, with John Young, remain with Rogers for three decades and become his principal associates. One of the first projects which the new team produced was the Aram Hospital (see p.101), an unbuilt scheme which, like the Zip-up enclosure, helped to establish the direction that the practice would take.

Chapter Five
Hunt and Rogers

In 1971, in collaboration with the engineers Ove Arup and Partners, Piano and Rogers won the competition for the cultural centre in the Place Beaubourg in Paris, subsequently known as the Centre Pompidou, and this was the project that brought Rogers into a position of international prominence. Despite the success of this building, the partnership with Piano did not last and from 1978 onwards Rogers practised under the name Richard Rogers and Partners.

The Lloyd's Headquarters building in London, completed in 1986 and also designed in collaboration with Ove Arup and Partners, was the first major building that Rogers built in the UK and it established him as one of the leading British architects of his generation. Rogers also completed the INMOS microprocessor factory in this period, this time with Tony Hunt. This was another prominent British building of the 1980s. In the 1990s the practice continued to attract an increasing volume of work, much of it concerned with the comprehensive redevelopment of large urban areas. Notable projects include masterplans for areas of Paris, London, Berlin and Shanghai, the European Court of Human Rights building in Strasbourg and the Channel 4 Headquarters building in London.

Rogers' approach to architecture has been discursive. Of the prominent British Modernists he is one of the few who has written about architecture and published books that were other than semi-autobiographical descriptions of his own work. His *Architecture: a modern view*[91] is a direct response to the call in the 1980s, from certain exalted lay quarters, for a return to the nostalgia of pre-twentieth century eclecticism. It also offers a robust if rather simplistic explanation of the reasons behind the failure of early Modernism: Rogers attributed the blame to the inability of clients to provide the circumstances of procurement in which good architecture can result. In *Cities for a small planet*,[92] which was a compilation of the series of Reith Lectures which he delivered on BBC Radio in 1995, he addressed the issue of the urban metropolis in the context of global ecology. Much of this book was concerned with the application of appropriate technology to the development of forms of architecture which were ecologically sustainable in the context of the urban conurbation.

Richard Rogers built fewer buildings with Tony Hunt than Norman Foster. For various reasons all of the major buildings which established him as a leading world architect were carried out in conjunction with Ove Arup and Partners as structural engineers and, in particular, with Peter Rice. The small number of buildings with which Tony Hunt was involved are, nevertheless, interesting. Hunt acted as engineer on all of the buildings that Rogers designed prior to the Centre Pompidou and several of these were crucial to his development as an architect. The buildings that Hunt designed with Rogers after Pompidou shed light on the differences of approach to architectural structure adopted by Hunt and Rice.

The early collaborations between Hunt and the Rogers practice

As with most practices, the early work of Richard and Su Rogers was concerned with small scale projects: they built private houses for relatives and friends and a number of small commercial buildings. All buildings of the early period between 1967 and 1971 were engineered by Tony Hunt.

The first projects undertaken by Richard and Su Rogers following the break up of Team 4 were the Spender and Rogers houses. These were designed with John Young who was greatly interested in developing the ideas on which the Reliance Controls building had been based. By the time of their design and construction, there was already a history of several decades of steel-frame houses[93] and even a steel house aesthetic based on exposure of the structure and transparency of the walls. The Spender and Rogers houses did, nevertheless, represent an innovative approach to house design in terms of spatial organisation and of the relationship between structure and cladding.

Although a house is a very different type of building from a factory, both the Spender and the Rogers houses shared many of the design intentions of the Reliance Controls building and both represented attempts to exploit contemporary technology to produce a thoroughly new type of house. Key intentions were the desire to preserve flexibility, so that the interiors could be adapted to the changing needs of the occupants, the elimination of wet trades, and the maximum use of industrially-made components selected from catalogues, to produce building envelopes which were quick and cheap to construct initially and easy to adapt subsequently. All of these considerations followed from Rogers' design philosophy, articulated in the 'manifesti'.

Due to common features in the clients' requirements, the two buildings were similarly arranged and each consisted of two enclosure units separated by a courtyard. The house is one of the units; in the Spender building the second unit was a studio whereas in the Rogers building it was a separate flatlet. Both houses had steel structures with unpunctured profiled-metal cladding on the side walls and fully glazed end walls. Internal partitions were non-structural and demountable. Both houses were based on arrangements of single-bay portal frameworks spanning 14 m across the entire width of the buildings with solid-web steel I-sections for both vertical and horizontal elements.

In the Spender House (Figs 5.2 and 5.3), which was the first to be constructed, the portal frameworks were connected at eaves level by an I-section purlin. The frames were self-bracing in their own plane, which was the across-building direction. Diagonal bracing rods were used as vertical-plane bracing in the side walls and acted in conjunction with the roof deck which provided bracing in the horizontal plane.

Photo: Anthony Hunt Associates

Fig. 5.3. Spender House, Utling, England. The vocabulary of Reliance Controls in the service of domestic architecture.

The Spender House was a direct translation of the Reliance Controls building into domestic architecture. It invites the question, how can that which is appropriate for a factory also be appropriate for a house? Interest of the client in Modern architecture is at least part of the answer. The building was remarkable for its commitment to the ideas of flexibility and the use of industrialised materials. The steel framework was placed outside the building envelope, which consisted of walls of either full-height glazing or plastic-coated, corrugated steel and a roof of plastic-coated, corrugated-steel decking. This combination of components allowed rapid initial construction and easy adaptability and extension because all elements of the enclosing membrane were demountable and moveable.

Chapter Five
Hunt and Rogers

Fig. 5.4. Rogers House, Wimbledon, England.

Photo: Anthony Hunt Associates

Fig. 5.5. Rogers House, Wimbledon, England. The lower flanges of the roof beams protrude through the ceiling. Rogers insisted that these should be of identical appearance even though the end beams carried half the load of the interior beams.

Photo: Anthony Hunt Associates

The Rogers House (*Figs 5.4 and 5.5*) was completed a year after the Spender House and, though similar, was significantly different. In this building the structure was placed inside the cladding envelope, to reduce maintenance, and the exterior was simpler and less cluttered in appearance. Diagonal bracing was eliminated and there was no secondary structure, the portal frames being linked structurally solely by the roof-deck panels. The wall panels spanned vertically between the ground-floor slab and the edge of the roof. Bracing in the along-building direction was provided by the roof and wall elements acting as stiff diaphragms.

Tony Hunt was asked to keep the section sizes of the steel portals as small as possible and also to make them identical in appearance. The second of these requirements was difficult to satisfy because the intermediate portals carried nearly double the load of the end portals. Hunt used the same basic I-sections for all portals and minimised the size required by using high-yield steel and also by means of full structural continuity of the beam-to-column connections. The strength of the intermediate portals was augmented by welding steel plates to the top flanges of the sections. These were not visible in the finished building, as only the lower flanges protruded through the ceiling, and so the illusion of identical structural elements was maintained — a clever, if 'dishonest', engineering expedient.

Another significant difference between the Spender and Rogers houses was the configuration of the cladding. In the Spender House this consisted of a conventional corrugated-steel outer skin with separate insulation and dry-liner layers. In the Rogers House a composite panel system, in which inner and outer skins were bonded to an insulating core, was used. In fact, this was a proprietary component which had been developed for refrigerated trucks and its use as the cladding of a building constituted an interesting piece of technology transfer.

The Spender and Rogers houses were made principally from prefabricated components and the use of 'wet' trades was minimised in their construction, but they were, nevertheless, one-off buildings which were hand-crafted to a considerable extent. The design and manufacturing processes were therefore laborious, especially the making of satisfactory junctions between components. Both Rogers and Hunt were interested in the idea of developing construction systems that were very simple to erect, flexible enough for use on any site and capable of meeting the requirements of any client. The Patera building, designed with Michael Hopkins, was perhaps Hunt's most serious exploration of this idea (see chapter 6). An entry for the 'House for Today' competition, run by the Du Pont Company in 1968, in which he collaborated with Rogers, provided an earlier opportunity to develop an industrialised building system.

The design that resulted was called 'Zip-up 1' and the idea was subsequently developed as 'Zip-up 2'. The key term was *zip-up*, which conveyed the idea of connecting parts of buildings quickly, simply and securely. It addressed one of the most problematic aspects of prefabrication, namely the making of satisfactory joints between components.

The Zip-up 1 house (*Fig. 5.1*) consisted of a single-volume enclosure formed by a stressed-skin monocoque shell resting on a steel underframe. The underframe, which was the interface between the building and the site, consisted of a horizontal deck of rectangular hollow-section beams supported by a square grid of columns. The latter had jacking units attached to their tops which allowed variations in level across the site to be accommodated. This was intended to minimise site preparation and to allow foundation work to be reduced to the removal of top-soil at each column base and the insertion of a paving-slab footing.

The most remarkable technical feature of the building was the monocoque enclosure. This was 10 m wide and consisted of panel units forming the walls, floor and roof in a wrap-around construction (*Fig. 5.6*). In a development of the cladding system used in the Rogers House, the need for a structural framework was eliminated entirely. Each panel consisted of two skins of aluminium alloy acting compositely with a core of expanded PVC. Detailed calculations carried out by Tony Hunt confirmed that this stressed-skin composite arrangement was very strong and rigid and thus capable of forming a self-supporting

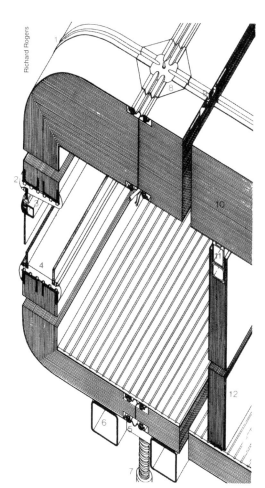

Fig. 5.6. Detail of the Zip-up enclosure showing the structural monocoque.

Fig. 5.7. Design Research Unit, London, England. The new top floor of this building was similar in appearance to the Zip-up enclosure but the arrangement was conventional with a steel framework supporting non-structural cladding.

enclosure. The overall thickness varied between panels, depending on the structural requirement; the thickest was the roof panel which had a depth of 150 mm to achieve a span of 10 m. The edges of the panels were detailed to allow transmission of structural loads through mechanical interlocking. Zip-up neoprene gaskets provided a weathertight seal. Openings in the panels could be cut by a power fret-saw and inserted either during or after construction. Glazing was retained by an extruded neoprene window surround. The thermal insulation performance of the self-supporting skin was excellent and in Zip-up 2 an autonomous house was envisaged complete with wind generator.

The Zip-up house system offered perhaps the ultimate in the flexible use of space. Internal partitions could be easily repositioned: they ran on retractable castors and were clipped to the underside of the roof panels by an inflatable locking tube. The bathroom and kitchen were serviced from below and could be relocated over a weekend. The planning strategy for the interior was to separate noisy and quiet areas by intermediate buffer zones.

The design was awarded second prize in the 'House for Today' competition which, given its novelty, was perhaps remarkable. To the regret of Tony Hunt, no Zip-up house was ever constructed:

'I have slight regrets about that, because I think if we'd been a bit clever, we actually could have got some money out of the British Steel Corporation or perhaps somebody else to pursue that. Although the climate in this country is such that it's almost impossible, even now, to get any interest in a building form such as that. Well, it's even more impossible now, I reckon. Which is pretty depressing, thinking its 20-odd years on.'[94]

Although the enclosure, together with its adjustable underframe, represented a new kind of shelter which should have attracted more general interest, Tony Hunt's assessment of the reason for its lack of appeal is probably accurate. It was just too different from most people's expectation of what a house should consist of to have become popular in Britain. It might possibly have had a future in a different application. It was, in effect, an industrialised version of a nomad's tent because it could have been erected on virtually any site and subsequently dismantled and removed leaving the site almost untouched by its presence. Being composed of lightweight components which were easily transportable and, given that the form was adaptable to different locations, it met all the requirements of a temporary building. It was, in other words, a solution to the problem of temporary rather than permanent housing. The former is always in demand somewhere in the world when disasters, natural or political, occur. The Zip-up idea could have been developed as a mass-produced, containerised temporary house.

The effort that went into Zip-up was not wasted because, rather in the way that happened with Foster and the unbuilt Newport School scheme, the ideas were used in subsequent projects that were built. In Rogers words: ' Zip-up begat UOP Fragrancies, not quite in its purest form but, nevertheless, a version of it.'[95]

In 1969 the firm of Richard and Su Rogers was commissioned to convert a four-storey building in central London for use by the Design Research Unit (DRU). This was principally a refurbishing job but it also involved the provision of extra accommodation by the addition of a storey to the existing building. This had to be of lightweight construction to minimise the load imposed on the existing structure and provided an opportunity to propose the building of a Zip-up enclosure on top of a building in central London. In this case the structure forming the monocoque was to have consisted of skins of glass-reinforced plastic with a phenolic core. It proved impossible to obtain building control approval for this arrangement, however, and the scheme that was built (*Fig. 5.7*) consisted of a fairly conventional aluminium cladding panel system, supported on a series of steel portal frameworks spanning the entire width of the building.

This outcome draws attention to the difficulties faced by designers who wish to introduce new technologies into building. With the Zip-up house, the problem had been that the form and general arrangement of the building were so different from those of the conventional house that no-one who was not firmly committed to Modernism was interested. At DRU the

Fig. 5.8. Universal Oil Products Factory, Tadworth, England. The architectural language is derived from the Zip-up enclosure but the building has a conventional arrangement with steel framework structure supporting non-structural cladding.

Fig. 5.9. Universal Oil Products Factory, Tadworth, England. Interior.

Fig. 5.10. Universal Oil Products Factory, Tadworth, England. The clean lines and extreme slenderness of the structural elements are well illustrated.

building control authority was reluctant to allow the construction of a system whose performance had not been thoroughly tested. Their position is understandable; in the interests of public safety the authorities must necessarily err on the side of caution. If the proposed DRU building had consisted of standard components, albeit in a novel arrangement, such as occurred at Reliance Controls or the Rogers and Spender houses, the authority might have been persuaded that its performance would be satisfactory. The use of a structural system that was completely new and untested, such as the Zip-up monocoque, was another matter.

This problem is unique to the building industry. In manufacturing industry there is an expectation that new products will be tested in prototype form and provision is made for the necessary research and development budget. Most buildings, however, are commissioned on a one-off basis by clients whose interest is in acquiring the accommodation rather than in funding the development of new building systems. There is therefore, in the case of innovative building technology applied to live projects, rarely enough money available to test new systems adequately before they are put into service. This aspect of the introduction of new technology into building was to be a constant problem for the High Tech architects. Sometimes, as with the DRU building, it resulted in a reversion to conventional systems with only the appearance of the new system being retained.

In other cases, systems were used which had not been adequately developed and whose subsequent performance proved to be unsatisfactory. A spectacular example of this occurred with Foster's Sainsbury Centre in which the purpose-designed cladding system failed within a few years of the completion of the building and had to be replaced, at great financial cost and also to the detriment of the building's appearance. It was fortunate that the Sainsbury family, which provided funding for both the original building and for its re-cladding, took a benign view of the situation.

The next project in which the Zip-up idea reappeared was a factory for Universal Oil Products at Tadworth in Surrey (*Figs 5.8* to *5.10*). The final version of the brief for this called for 1700 m^2 of light industrial building including administration, laboratory, compounds and stores for the production of fragrances. Speed of construction, low cost of both construction and maintenance, and a high resale value were important considerations. In the final design the building was a single-storey shed of deep rectangular plan.

As in the case of the DRU building, the monocoque arrangement was not used because the large size of the building, precluded the possibility of a self-supporting envelope. A conventional arrangement, in which a steel frame supported a non-structural cladding system, was adopted. The structure consisted of a primary/secondary grid of purpose-made

triangulated girders welded from hollow-section, hot-rolled steel. The cladding was wrap-around, with similar panels being used on the walls and roof. As with contemporary buildings by Foster, no eaves gutters or downpipes were required. The skins of the cladding panels were of glass-reinforced cement, a novel material at the time. Its rapid installation allowed a weathertight shell to be created quickly. The principal feature to survive from the original Zip-up design was the appearance rather than the technology.

INMOS Microprocessor Factory

The INMOS building was the first of two distinctive industrial buildings[96] designed by Richard Rogers and Partners that were based on a central services spine with a steel exoskeleton in which long-span girders were supported, in part, by an arrangement of masts and tension elements. Both drew heavily on the ideas formulated in the design of an unbuilt scheme for a hospital which Tony Hunt had worked on with the Rogers team in the early 1970s. This was the Aram Module (*Fig. 5.11*) – a scheme for a portable hospital which could be transported anywhere but which was envisaged principally for use in the Third World. It involved the use of a steel masted exoskeleton supporting a building envelope in such a way as to minimise the intrusion of structure into the enclosed space. It was the precursor of INMOS:

'Out of Aram you could almost argue INMOS.'[97]

Photo: Anthony Hunt Associates

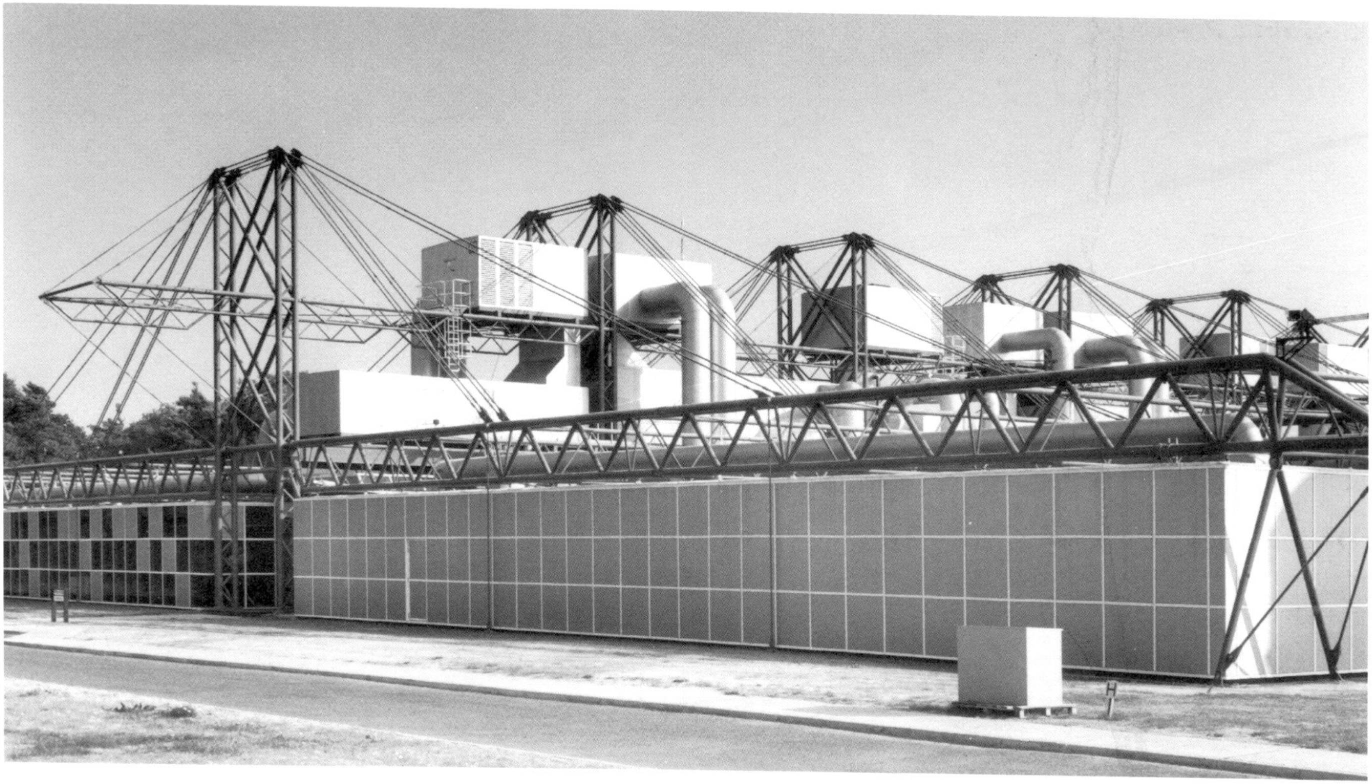

Fig. 5.12. INMOS Microprocessor Factory, Newport, Wales. Richard Rogers and Partners, 1982.

Richard Rogers

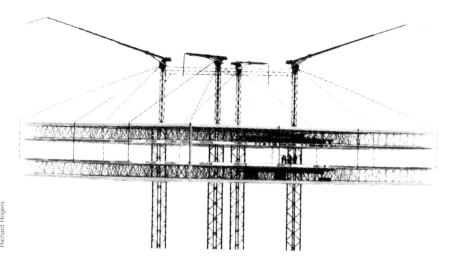

Fig. 5.11. The Aram Project was an early unbuilt scheme by Rogers and Hunt which anticipated arrangements used in later exoskeletal buildings.

The building for the INMOS Microprocessing Company (*Fig. 5.12*) provided a manufacturing and dispatch facility for advanced microchips, together with associated administrative and support accommodation. Particular requirements specified by the client were that the design and construction should be carried out quickly and that provision should be made for exceptionally clean and dust-free air quality in the production areas which occupied 50% of the floor area. Additional design objectives required of themselves by the architects were the familiar list common to Rogers, Foster and other High Tech architects, namely that the design process should be capable of responding to changes in the brief as the design evolved, that a stimulating and friendly environment should be created for the employees and that the final design should allow maximum flexibility in the way in which the spaces were used and in its potential for subsequent change or growth.

The plan of the building is simple and is similar to those of the single-storey sheds built by Foster in the 1970s. It is based on a linear arrangement with a central spine housing the main circulation route and servicing plant (*Fig. 5.13*). The production area was located on one side of the spine and the administrative and ancillary accommodation occupied a more-or-less equal floor area on the other. The building is single storey throughout but the spine has three levels, two of them for plant above the roof of the central corridor.

Photo: Anthony Hunt Associates

Fig. 5.13. INMOS Microprocessor Factory, Newport, Wales. Spinal circulation route.

Photo: Anthony Hunt Associates

Fig. 5.14. INMOS Microprocessor Factory, Newport, Wales. The outer ends of the main structural elements are supported on bi-pod struts which help to stabilise the structure.

Apart from two rows of columns in the central spine the structure is placed entirely outside the building's envelope as are the main heating and ventilating systems. The air-supply systems are grouped in localised modules above the central circulation route, and ducts running at right angles to the spine, above the roof but within the structural zone, deliver air to the points of use. Production waste is collected in floor ducts running under the production area parallel to the central spine.

The structure is a steel framework whose layout is well integrated with the general arrangement of the accommodation. The primary elements are a series of nine towers ranged along the central spine. These each consist of two pairs of circular hollow-section columns braced

together and the towers are linked longitudinally by two sets of horizontal elements supporting the two-level air-handling plant. The towers are stabilised in both the along-building and the across-building directions by cross-bracing and are therefore entirely self-supporting. The exoskeletal roof structure over the main accommodation consists of primary beams which span the entire distance of 38 m from the central spine to the edge of the building and are supported on the spine towers at the inner end and by bi-pod arrangements of struts at the outer end (*Fig. 5.14*). The primary beams are also supported at the third-span points by tension elements attached to the tops of the spine towers (*Fig. 5.15*). These primary elements are in balanced pairs, one on either side of the spine.

Fig. 5.15. INMOS Microprocessor Factory, Newport, Wales. The structure is external to the cladding to preserve ultra-clean air conditions in the interior.

Secondary elements are provided at 6 m centres spanning between the main girders and these carry the profiled-steel-sandwich roof deck. All main structural elements are triangulated girders composed of hollow-section steel elements.

The space planning and the general arrangement of both the structure and the services were dictated by the requirements of the programme. The placing of the structure and services outside the skin of the building allowed an ultra-clean environment to be created in the production areas. It also facilitated access to services for maintenance and repair without disruption of the production areas. This was essential in view of the envisaged 24-hour operation of the plant.

The use of a long-span structure was justified in the interests of maintaining the production area free of internal structure, and the fact that this area represented 50% of the total justified the spinal arrangement with balanced structure to either side. The structure-free interior of the long-span exoskeleton was consistent with the ideas expressed in Rogers' manifesto of 1969 which were first tried in the Aram Module project.

Anthony Hunt Associates, in the manner that was by this time customary, responded well to the engineering challenge. The structure of the INMOS building was justifiable from a technical viewpoint, given the spans and loads involved. The adoption of steel as the structural material and the use of the binary arrangement of triangulated girders supported by an arrangement

of masts and tension elements was entirely appropriate.

Several aspects of the structure were innovatory and contributed to both its visual and technical success. Very careful attention was paid to the detailing of connections so that the erection process would proceed smoothly. The steelwork was prefabricated by welding but the site joints were made with single pins, washers and split pins rather than by bolting or welding (*Figs 5.16* and *5.17*). This gave smaller and more elegant joints and greatly simplified the erection sequence. Several of the joint elements were formed in cast steel, also unusual at this time and developed subsequently by Hunt in the Patera and Waterloo Terminal buildings. Casting was more economical than machining due to the high level of repetition that occurred and it produced more elegant joints than would have been possible by welding components together. Much effort was expended by the Hunt team in the detailing of the structure which is one of the most elegant that they have produced.

Rogers and Hunt

Although Tony Hunt built fewer buildings with Rogers than he did with Foster, the buildings described in this chapter were, nevertheless, highly significant in the development of Rogers' individual style. The early buildings, the Spender and Rogers houses, the Zip-up enclosure and the UOP building, were all heavily influenced by the earlier work at Team 4. Preoccupation with the refining of design ideas is discernible in the progressive development of cladding systems from the Reliance-like Spender house through the Rogers house to the self-supporting composite panels that formed the Zip-up enclosures. Although the ideas invested in these projects were important, this particular line of development did not in fact lead anywhere for Rogers. Neither of the built projects that followed from Zip-up (DRU or UOP) was in the true spirit of the original, and there were to be no similar buildings. It is tempting to see here the influence of Foster because all of these buildings are Foster-like in the sense that emphasis is placed on the production of jewel-like, immaculately detailed enclosures. The

future for Rogers had its origins in the unbuilt Aram Hospital project (also referred to as the Aram Module) and, with hindsight, it is obvious that this is what he really wanted to do.

Rogers' opportunity to make this kind of architecture occurred in spectacular fashion with the winning of the competition for the Centre Pompidou . This building expresses the idea that the combination of functions in the constituent elements of a building should be avoided. Here, structure is structure and only structure and the same is true of cladding and services. The building is an assembly of single-function components; all are accessible, allowing maintenance, change and replacement to be carried out easily and to different timescales and this is vigorously expressed. The building is easily readable and each component proclaims its function.

With this type of architecture Rogers broke free from the influence of Foster, found his own architectural voice and began to make the kind of built form that he had envisaged in his manifesto of 1969. It is an approach to architecture that he has followed consistently since, with the Lloyd's Headquarters building in London being a particularly spectacular example. The fact that it had first appeared in the Aram Hospital which Rogers designed with Hunt shows that Hunt was once again in at the beginning, working closely with an architect as he evolved the vocabulary that would become his personal style. It is perhaps a matter for

Fig. 5.16. INMOS Microprocessor Factory, Newport, Wales. All site joints were pinned for ease of assembly.

regret that, due to chance, Hunt was not to collaborate with Rogers in a built project of this kind until INMOS, ten years after the ideas on which it was based were jointly formulated in the unbuilt Aram project.

As a footnote to this chapter it is interesting to note that Hunt's collaboration with Rogers over INMOS makes an illuminating comparison with the very different work that he carried out a little earlier with Foster on the Sainsbury Centre. These two buildings illustrate that he was able both to accommodate the particular agendas of the two architects and to produce engineering that was appropriate. In contrasting the two buildings, Rogers said:

'If an engineer is working on one side with an exposed structuralist and on another side with an architect who is by nature a skin architect then you are not going to be able to convince the skin architect to become a structuralist nor the structuralist to become a skin architect but in both of those the good engineer will add tremendous richness to that approach.'[98]

The 'richness' that Tony Hunt contributed to Sainsbury and Inmos was a structure that performed well technically and that was visually both spectacular and elegant.

Photo: Anthony Hunt Associates

Fig. 5.17. INMOS Microprocessor Factory, Newport, Wales. Pinned connection between tie rods and the main structural elements.

Chapter Six
Hunt and Hopkins

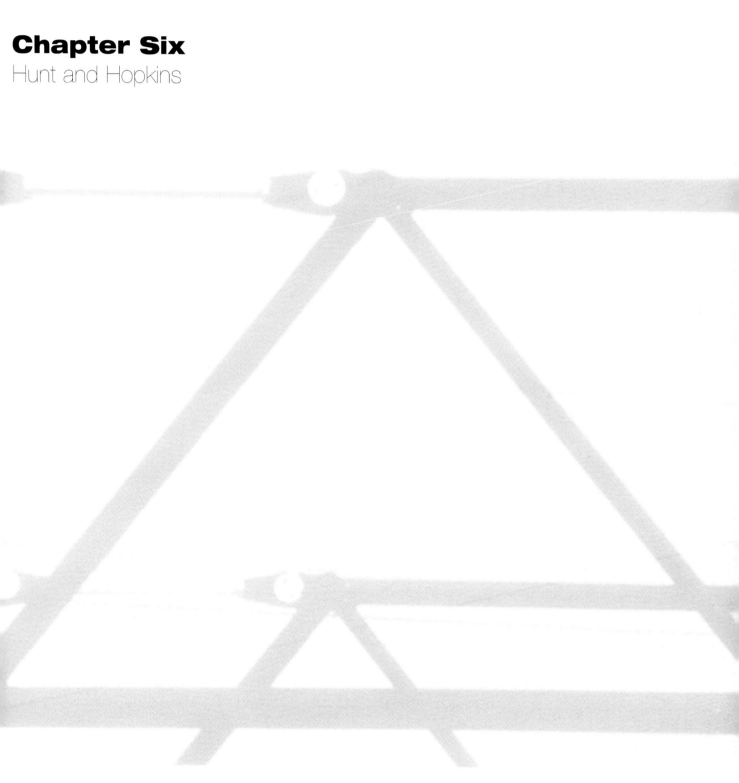

Chapter Six
Hunt and Hopkins

Introduction

Although it is probably correct to regard Norman Foster and Richard Rogers as the creators of the style that became known as British High Tech, this view is a little misleading because it fails to give due recognition to the roles played by Michael Hopkins and by Tony Hunt. In the late 1970s and early 1980s, the most vigorous period of High Tech, Hopkins was less well known than Foster or Rogers because, despite being of a similar age, he did not set up in practice in his own right until 1976, nine years later than they had done. For eight of those years he was in partnership with Foster and made important contributions to several of the buildings that helped to establish the Foster practice, including the IBM building at Cosham and the Willis, Faber and Dumas building in Ipswich.

The son of a builder, Hopkins developed an interest in architecture at an early age. His formal architectural education was at the Architectural Association in London from which he graduated in 1963. He joined Foster as a partner in Foster Associates in 1968 and immediately became involved in the design of the IBM building at Cosham. This was congenial work because Hopkins had by this time become greatly interested in making buildings either from 'found' components selected from catalogues or from technologies that were developed jointly with component manufacturers. The influences were the same ones as had worked on Foster and Rogers, principally the Californian Case Study Houses and the Schools Construction Systems Development project (SCSD). The IBM building gave him direct experience of this approach.

In 1976, Hopkins founded his own practice with his architect wife Patty. Four significant buildings established the style of the firm: these were the house at Hampstead, London that the Hopkins built for themselves and that also served initially as their office, the Green King Draft Beer Cellar at Bury St Edmonds, the Patera Building System and the Schlumberger Research Laboratories in Cambridge. Tony Hunt was the structural engineer for all these projects.

The Hopkins House

The Hopkins House, with its exposed steel framework and its transparent walls (*Fig. 6.1*), was an unashamed celebration of the industrialised basis of Modern society, of the 'new' materials of glass and steel, of mass production of components and of the house as a 'machine for living'. It also represented an almost complete repudiation of any preconceived notions of architectural composition. The positioning of the entrance off-centre in the third of six bays, for example, seems almost perverse from an aesthetic viewpoint. The approach was well articulated in the book on Hopkins by Colin Davies:

'Within the design parameters established by Michael and Patty Hopkins, their house, in its strategic form, "designed itself". The building zone is defined by the street and garden building lines, which are just over 10 metres apart. At the sides the house is pulled back 1 metre from the adjoining buildings to avoid any party-wall conditions. The house is two storeys high; one floor, originally the Hopkins' office, is entered at street level, and the other at garden level beneath.'[99]

This pragmatic approach was carried through to the selection and detailing of elements and the roles of the architects were reduced almost to those of technical facilitators; there were no golden sections, harmonic proportions, axes of symmetry or indeed any of the aspects of form that originate in conventional aesthetic theory.

The building was on two floors; it had a rectangular plan measuring 12 m by 10 m and initially served both as an office and as a home for Michael and Patty Hopkins and their three children (*Fig. 6.2*). The entrance was at the upper level into the large open-plan space that was both living accommodation and office. Kitchen, dining and bedroom areas were at the lower level entered directly from the garden. The external walls on the long sides of the building were fully glazed; the end walls, which face adjoining buildings, were covered with two skins of profiled steel wall cladding separated by 40 mm of fibreglass insulation infill.

The structure was a two-storey steel frame supporting floor and roof decks which consisted, in each case, of profiled steel sheeting topped with composite boarding (*Figs 6.3 and 6.4*). Chipboard and fibreboard were used in the floor and insulating board in the roof. The overall plan

Fig. 6.1. The Hopkins House, Hampstead, London, England. Garden elevation.

Photo: Anthony Hunt Associates

Fig. 6.2. The Hopkins House, Hampstead, London, England. Interior.

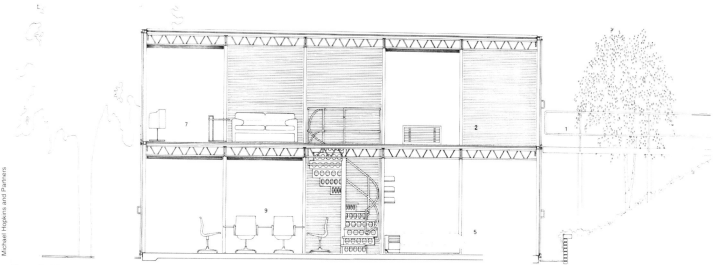

Michael Hopkins and Partners

Fig. 6.3. The Hopkins House, Hampstead, London, England. Section showing the post-and-beam structure.

dimensions of 10 m by 12 m were subdivided into a 2 m by 4 m rectangular column grid with the profiled decks spanning the short sides of the rectangles.

The steel frame consisted of lightweight triangulated trusses spanning directly between the columns. Contrary to appearances, these were not off-the-peg standard components selected from a catalogue but were specially made for the project by a local steelwork fabricator. Identical sections were used throughout with no distinction being made between floor and roof structures or between the trusses which actually carried the weights of the floor and roof and those which were linking elements. Similarly, all columns were identical 60 mm by 60 mm rolled hollow sections with welded fully-rigid beam-to-column connections. There was no secondary structure: the floor, roof and external wall systems were attached directly to the primary structural framework. The triangulated beams were site-welded to the columns to form continuous horizontal girders.

Vertical-plane bracing of the diagonal type was provided in two bays in each of the glazed walls. The cladding on the unglazed walls served as diaphragm vertical-plane bracing in the across-building direction. The floor and roof decks acted as horizontal-plane bracing. There were no permanent internal partitions on the upper level; the interior was divided by Venetian blinds suspended from the steel girders. Solid partitions were provided between the bedrooms

on the ground floor. A considerable degree of standardisation was present in the structure as well as in other aspects of the building, which contributed to its being constructed easily, quickly and at relatively low cost.

The use of a steel frame for a house, which in the UK would more normally be constructed in some combination of masonry and timber, was unusual and must be judged an unconventional structure for a building of this size. It was, of course, selected here mainly for aesthetic and stylistic reasons but the architects argued convincingly[100] that it also provided a thoroughly practical and economic solution to their particular requirements, which were for a relatively large house of predominantly open plan which could be erected in a minimum time and at a reasonable cost.

The structure performs well when judged by purely technical criteria. The degree of efficiency achieved was appropriate: spans were short, which justified the use of a post-and-beam arrangement, but loads were light, which justified the use of measures to increase efficiency, such as the statically indeterminate rigid-joint configuration and the triangulated beam profiles. The standardisation of beam and column sizes, which reduced efficiency, was also justified on the grounds of cost and appearance, because an appropriate degree of efficiency was provided in other ways. The use of a steel frame allowed a completely open plan and met the requirement for fast erection, neither of which

could have been achieved so well by the use of a conventional masonry and/or timber structure. The degree of standardisation mitigated the potentially increased cost which the use of steel framing for a building of this size might otherwise have caused and the relatively high efficiency which was achieved also helped to reduce costs. The structure was therefore a sensible compromise.

The success of the Hopkins house as a work of architecture was due in no small measure to the cleverness of the engineering. The adoption of a small-span column grid allowed lightweight beam elements to be used and the continuity offered by the all-welded construction enhanced their efficiency. The use of diagonal and diaphragm bracing in the vertical planes relieved the columns of bending moment due to lateral loading and allowed very slender elements to be selected. The use of composite action between the profiled metal floor and roof decks and their board coverings improved efficiency and lowered the construction depth. These were all devices that were, by the mid 1970s, hallmarks of steel frameworks designed by Tony Hunt, who was relentless, as had been his mentor Samuely, in his pursuit of ever more highly refined, lighter and more slender structural elements. Given the highly pragmatic approach being adopted by the architects, it might be said that the architecture here was very largely dependent on the qualities of Tony Hunt's structure.

Fig. 6.4. The Hopkins House, Hampstead, London. Construction shot showing the relationship between the structural framework and the steel decking. The latter act compositely with the floor and roof boarding to reduce structural depth. Vertical-plane bracing (cross-bracing in the side walls and diaphragm bracing in the end walls) allowed very slender columns to be used by relieving them of wind loading.

Green King Draft Beer Cellar

The Green King Draft Beer Cellar building houses plant for cleaning and filling draft beer kegs and is part of the Green King brewery at Bury St Edmunds, Suffolk (*Fig. 6.5*). It is essentially a large, single-volume shed whose internal layout was determined by the process carried on within it. The plan is rectilinear with loading bays at either end. Empty kegs are delivered at one end and pass through zones in which they are cleaned, filled and stored before being loaded into dray lorries at the other end (*Fig. 6.6*). Small-

volume spaces, such as staff rest-rooms, are located in small enclosures within the building.

The reinforced-concrete floor slab of the building was raised above ground level on a grid of piles because the building is situated on the flood plain of the River Linnet. It corresponds to the tailgate height of beer lorries and is cantilevered at each end of the building to form the loading docks. The superstructure is a steel framework with perimeter columns set back from the side walls to provide corridor zones running the entire length of the building, an arrangement that recalls earlier buildings by Foster. Side walls are of profiled metal sandwich panels which span horizontally between mullions fixed to the floor slab and roof structure. The end walls are full-height with transparent roller shutter doors set back from the edges of the floor and roof structures to provide covered loading bays. The roof deck is of profiled metal.

The primary elements of the building's superstructure are three 6-bay portal frameworks which run its entire length, one adjacent to each side wall and one on the centreline. The horizontal parts of these are triangulated Warren girders made up from square and circular hollow-section sub-elements welded. The vertical parts of the portal frames are circular hollow-section columns. These frameworks support a series of secondary elements of similarly configured Warren girders on which the roof deck is mounted. Primary and secondary elements are of equal depth and the frame is self-bracing by virtue of the rigid beam-to-column connections. The general arrangement of the structure is very similar to that of the Hopkins House.

The steelwork was prefabricated by welding and bolted together on site. The neatness of the detailing that was achieved with the bolted connections of this building was remarkable (*Fig. 6.7*). The architectural quality of the building stems from the elegance of the proportions and the refinement of the detailing. As in the case of the Hopkins House the qualities of the exposed structure were crucial to its success.

John Winter, writing in the *Architectural Review* at a time when British industry was facing a period of significant change, said of the Green King building:

'The Green King plant is a silver package for packaging set in a lovely Suffolk town. The great centres of British industry with their low productivity and their sordid cities have not yet approached our younger, more adventurous architects. Wake up, Birmingham!'[101]

The Patera building

The above quotation from John Winter's review of the Green King building makes a fitting introduction to the next project that Hopkins worked on with Hunt, which was the Patera building. This was an attempt to address the problem of the poor architectural quality of most industrial estates in Britain.

In the 1980s the character of British industry changed. The traditional industries —

Fig. 6.7. The Green King Draft Beer Cellar, Bury St Edmonds, England.

Fig. 6.5. The Green King Draft Beer Cellar, Bury St Edmonds, England.

Fig. 6.6. The Green King Draft Beer Cellar, Bury St Edmonds, England.

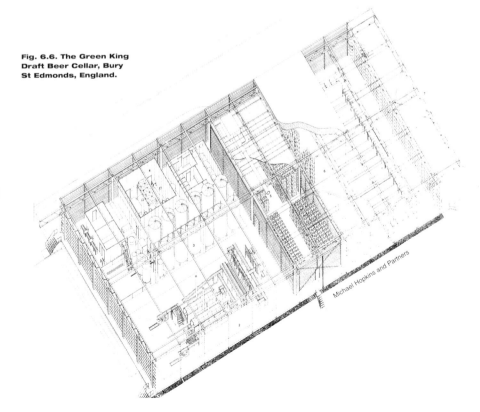

steel, shipbuilding, textiles, coal mining — were in terminal decline and were being replaced by 'clean' industries, such as those associated with microelectronics, which were diverse and which operated on an altogether smaller scale. This transition created a need for a new type of small industrial building which consisted essentially of an open area in which production could take place with an office attached. The Patera building (*Fig. 6.8*) was intended to satisfy this need.

Patera was not just a building: it was also the core of an idea for a new kind of environment for industry. The early industrial buildings of Foster, Hopkins, Hunt and Rogers had brought into being a new factory aesthetic and had shown that modern commercial buildings could be beautiful as well as economic and practical. The majority of the buildings that were created for the new clean industries were, nevertheless, designed in an atmosphere in which little consideration was given to appearance or indeed to any aspect of the built environment that was concerned with the wellbeing of their users. The jewel-like buildings of the founders of High Tech, which were mostly located in industrial estates, were surrounded by buildings which constituted a kind of late twentieth-century vernacular in which forms were determined by the forces of economics untempered by any aesthetic considerations. The problem was not so much that beautiful buildings could not be created from the products of industry — Foster and Rogers had shown that they could — but of a complete

Photo: Anthony Hunt Associates

Fig. 6.8. The Patera building. One of the prototypes following its erection in London's Docklands.

lack of concern for the aesthetics of the environment by the people who commissioned industrial buildings. The Patera concept sought to address this issue. It encompassed not just the idea of the well-designed industrial building but also that of an industrial estate that would constitute an uplifting environment.

Patera was the brainchild of Nigel Dale, a businessman with interests in metal structures but who had some inside knowledge of architecture because he had spent some time as an architecture student in the early 1970s. By the time the Patera project was initiated Nigel Dale's background was in the field of industrial production, a world in which products were developed and perfected through the building and testing of prototypes

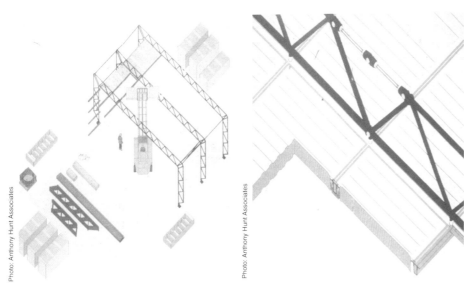

Photo: Anthony Hunt Associates

Photo: Anthony Hunt Associates

Fig. 6.9. The Patera building was designed for quick and simple assembly using no item of plant larger than a fork-lift truck.

Fig. 6.11. The Patera building. The purlins and cladding rails are located within the cladding zone.

Fig. 6.10. The main structural elements of the Patera building form a hybrid two-hinge/three-hinge portal framework which is located outside the cladding.

Photo: Anthony Hunt Associates

and which were made commercially successful through market research and marketing. His intention was to apply these techniques to industrial architecture — an idea of which the early Modernists would have thoroughly approved and which had already been attempted several times in the twentieth century although never with much success.

Dale's idea was to produce a building system that would be economic, flexible and stylish and to link this to a development company that would act as the co-ordinator of industrial estates. The development company would acquire land, design a layout of building plots and install infrastructure. Individual tenant clients would then have buildings tailor-made to their requirements within a consistent style offered by a building system. The buildings would, in effect, be industrial apartments capable of being adapted to different client requirements and offered for rent for varying lengths of tenure to suit clients' needs. It was also intended that the development company would provide centralised management services such as telephone switchboard facilities, catering and computer services together with maintenance of both buildings and landscape.

The principal hardware element in the concept was a basic building shell which could be erected and fitted out quickly to meet the needs of an individual tenant and then easily adapted to suit the requirements of subsequent tenants. It was envisaged that the scale of the operation would allow the building to be treated as an industrial product; it would be developed and tested in prototype form and subsequently manufactured in sufficient numbers to cover its development costs. Michael Hopkins was commissioned as architect and Tony Hunt as structural engineer.

It was envisaged that the erection of the building would occur in three phases. The first of these was the laying of a rectangular foundation and ground-floor slab in which services would be incorporated. This was the interface between the superstructure and the site that rendered the building non-site-specific. The building could be built anywhere that this standard rectangular slab could be laid. The second stage was the erection of the superstructure, a shell of cladding — incorporating trunking for electrical and telephone services — supported on a steel framework (Fig. 6.9). The third stage was the subdivision and fitting out of the interior to meet specific client requirements. The major design effort went into the superstructure which would constitute the second stage and Hopkins and Hunt were principally concerned with its creation. The building that they developed was sophisticated and stylish. It consisted of two more-or-less independent systems — cladding and structure — for which Hopkins and Hunt were respectively responsible.

The structure consisted of a series of triangulated portal frameworks, which spanned 13·2 m across the building (Fig. 6.10), linked by rectangular hollow-section purlins and cladding rails spaced 1·2 m apart and spanning 3·6 m between the main frames.[102] The cladding of the roof and side walls consisted of identical panels measuring 1·2 m by 3·6 m bolted to the purlins and cladding rails (Fig. 6.11). Each panel consisted of two skins of steel sheet, corrugated for increased rigidity, separated by a 150 mm wide internal cavity filled with mineral fibre.

The relationship between structure and cladding was interesting, with the triangulated main frames placed externally and the purlins and cladding rails occupying the same zone as the cladding itself. This produced an exterior which was interesting visually and an interior which was entirely uncluttered and which allowed maximum flexibility in the use of space (Fig. 6.12). It also meant that the structure was protected from fire by the cladding which gave the building the required half-hour fire rating.

The main frameworks were ingeniously designed to meet exacting performance requirements which called for a structure that would be of stylish appearance with, for ease of containerisation, no element longer than 6·75 m and, for ease of construction, no elements heavier than could be lifted by a fork-lift truck.[103] To meet these requirements a hybrid two-hinge/three-hinge portal framework was chosen. The inherent efficiency of this form, together with the full triangulation of the elements and the relatively small ratio of span to depth that was adopted allowed very slender

Fig. 6.12. The very clean lines of the interior of the Patera building were made possible by placing the cladding rails and purlins within the cladding zone.

Fig. 6.13. The two-pin site connection between the vertical and horizontal parts of the primary structure of the Patera building allowed a rigid joint to be made that was easy to assemble.

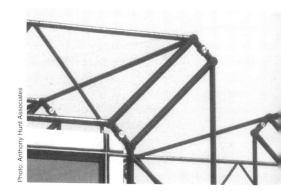

circular hollow-section sub-elements to be used. Each portal consisted of two horizontal and two vertical sub-units which were prefabricated by welding. Cast-steel jointing components allowed very precise pin-type site connections to be developed and these were cleverly arranged at the junction between the horizontal and vertical elements to provide a rigid connection there (*Fig. 6.13*).

The hybrid two-hinge/three-hinge arrangement (*Fig. 6.10*) was adopted to eliminate the need for additional lateral bracing of the compression side of the structure by ensuring that the inner booms of the main elements, which were restrained laterally by the cladding, remained in compression under all conditions of loading. The key to this behaviour was an ingenious three-pin tension-only link between the top elements of the portal at the central joint (*Fig. 6.14*). Under gravitational load, this was subjected to compression and collapsed to produce a hinge joint between the main elements at the mid-span position which ensured that compression was concentrated in the inner booms of the frame. If load reversal occurred, due to wind uplift, reversal of stress within the structure did not occur because the tension-only link now became part of the structure and converted the main frame to a two-hinge arrangement because the mid-span joint between the horizontal elements became rigid. It meant that the laterally-restrained inner boom remained in compression and that most

of the outer boom continued to be subjected only to tension. Some compression did occur in the outer boom, in the vicinity of the knee joint, but the greater efficiency of the two-hinge arrangement, together with the low internal forces that occurred in response to wind loading, ensured that these were not sufficiently large to initiate instability. Lateral restraint, in the form of cross-bracing between two of the frames, was, nevertheless, provided at this level and also served to stabilise the building in the longitudinal direction. The main frames were, of course, self-bracing in the across-building direction.

The purlins and cladding rails were rectangular hollow-section elements with angle sections welded to their edges to serve as fixings for the cladding panels. Connections to the main frames were effected by internally threaded cylindrical units welded to purlins, cladding rails and main frame elements. The connections themselves were made by double-ended bolts with the threads at each end operating in the opposite sense to allow simultaneous tightening with one direction of rotation.

A feature of the structure was the extremely fine tolerances which were specified: erection tolerances were ± 1 mm with structure; fabrication tolerances of ± 0.5 mm and component tolerances of ± 0.25 mm. Gaskets were manufactured to accommodate tolerances and movement in the range + 1 mm to − 3 mm. Such tolerances belong to the world of

mechanical engineering rather than to that of building construction and are an indication of the design philosophy.

The building, taken as a whole, was an industrial product rather than an assembly of the products of industry (*Fig. 6.15*). It underwent several stages of development. Firstly, a mock-up was constructed in the factory and then two full-size prototypes were erected outside the factory.[104] The experience gained with these allowed the manufacturing process to be refined.

The Patera building did not succeed commercially and opinions differ concerning the reason for this. One explanation is that it was because Nigel Dale, who had commissioned it, lost interest in the project. Following the completion of the prototypes, and despite considerable interest shown in the system, he dropped the idea and discontinued the marketing effort. With the benefit of hindsight it can be concluded that this was the main cause of its demise. The Patera building was a component part of an idea for a new type of industrial estate. Without the backup of a development company that would initiate and co-ordinate the setting up of industrial estates, the economies of scale that would have been required to manufacture such a sophisticated system economically would not have been realised. Deprived of this 'infrastructure' the building would have had to have been sold to clients on an individual basis and, given its level of sophistication, would not have been able to

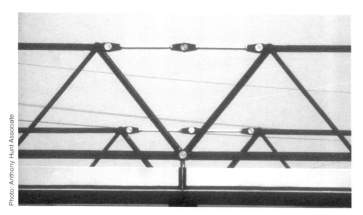

Fig. 6.14. The three-hinge tension-only link at the mid-span position of the horizontal elements in the Patera building made the joint behave as a hinge under downward acting load and as a rigid joint under upward acting load. This meant that the laterally-restrained lower booms of the trusses remained in compression under all conditions of load.

Fig. 6.15. The cladding and structure of the Patera building were visually stylish.

compete with the many other building systems that exploited the market for small-scale industrial buildings.

The Patera building has been criticised from a technical viewpoint but much of this has stemmed from a failure to understand the total Patera concept. Attention has been drawn to the complexity of the components — for example, the cladding rails with their bolted connectors which would have been relatively expensive to produce. In the context of the envisaged mass production, however, and the consequent economies of scale that this would have allowed, this was not really a valid criticism. A more serious criticism was the possible lack of weathertightness of the cladding. This is frequently a problem where the same system is used for both wall and roof cladding. In the Patera building the potential inadequacy of the gaskets to serve as effective waterproof seals, especially on the flat roof, was an obvious cause for concern. This was demonstrated to be justified when Hopkins used the Patera cladding system, though not the structure, for new offices built for his practice in Marylebone, London, once it had outgrown the house in Hampstead. Here the problems of lack of weathertightness quickly emerged in the flat roof. These problems would no doubt have been overcome, however, had the system gone into large-scale production.

Michael Hopkins acquired the patents to the Patera system following Nigel Dale's loss of interest. Tony Hunt still believes that it has the potential for commercial success. It was a remarkable building concept — stylish, ingenious, adaptable and a genuine attempt to apply the standards of industrial manufacture at the scale of the whole building. It required the collaboration of Hopkins and Hunt to develop it, drawing on their experience of a decade earlier at IBM Cosham — a building with which the system has a certain amount in common — but it has so far failed to capture the imagination of a developer with the vision and imagination to realise the kind of commercial or industrial estate that would make it economically viable.

Photo: Anthony Hunt Associates

Fig. 6.16. The Schlumberger Research Centre, Cambridge, England.

The Schlumberger building

The building for the Schlumberger Company (*Figs 6.16* and *6.17*), the last in which Hunt and Hopkins have collaborated to date, was a centre specialising in research into aspects of oil exploration. The brief called for four types of accommodation: laboratories, individual offices for scientists, a drilling-rig testing station and staff recreation facilities. Hopkins placed the testing station in the centre of the building and flanked it with the laboratories and staff rooms in two single-storey wings 24 m apart. Each had a spinal corridor with laboratories on one side, facing the testing station, and staff rooms on the other, adjacent to the external walls.

The structural arrangement of the flanking wings was straightforward and similar to that adopted in the Patera building. Triangulated-truss primary elements, above the roof deck, spanned between circular hollow-section columns located adjacent to the exterior walls. The refinements of the Patera structure — the hybrid two-hinge/three-hinge portal frames and the sophisticated pinned connections between elements were dispensed with. The roof deck was a conventional waterproof membrane supported on a profiled metal deck. End walls were of profiled-metal cladding. The side walls consisted of full-height glazing in the form of sliding partitions.

Perhaps the most distinctive feature of the Schlumberger building was the roof of the testing station which consisted of three tent-like membranes of teflon-coated glass fibre supported on a network of masts and cables. This was, in fact, a late development of the design. Earlier versions had a space-deck arrangement designed by Hunt. In the final version Hunt was responsible for only the membrane support structure — the membrane itself was designed by Ove Arup and Partners.

Hopkins and Hunt

In previous chapters it was shown that Hunt played a crucial role in the establishment of Norman Foster and Richard Rogers. The same was true of Hopkins. Not only was Hunt the engineer on the buildings which Hopkins produced with Foster, he also acted as the engineer for early buildings of Hopkins' independent practice which were crucial to the establishment of its reputation. The Hopkins House, which received extensive publicity, played an especially important role in this. The significance of the engineering cannot be overemphasised. Such elegance as the building possesses is mainly dependent on the structure.

Fig. 6.17. The Schlumberger Research Centre, Cambridge, England. AHA were responsible for the design of all of the steelwork. The fabric membrane was designed by Ove Arup and Partners.

Chapter Seven
Hunt and Grimshaw

Chapter Seven
Hunt and Grimshaw

Introduction

Late Modern metal and glass architecture was dependent on the expression of structure and therefore on the type of high quality engineering that Tony Hunt could produce. Of the British architects who made their reputations in the 1970s and 80s as the masters of this style, Nicholas Grimshaw was the one with whom Hunt has carried out the fewest projects. He and Grimshaw had known each other since 1968, when Hunt acted as structural engineer for a block of flats which Grimshaw had designed for a housing association in London. It was one of Grimshaw's first commissions and, like those of his contemporaries who were also to become leaders of their profession in Britain, was both innovative architecturally and favourably received by the critics. Despite this successful collaboration, however, the professional paths of Hunt and Grimshaw did not cross again for over 20 years. When they did, the result was one of the most outstanding buildings of late twentieth-century British architecture — the International Railway Terminal at Waterloo Station in London, completed in 1993. This remarkable building could only have been created by a team like Grimshaw and Hunt and it may be regarded as the result of the flowering of the talents and skills that had been built up in their respective practices over the previous two decades.

From Tony Hunt's point of view, Grimshaw's practice was an ideal group with which to collaborate due to their attitude to the relationship which should exist between architecture and engineering. In Grimshaw's words:

'We are a very engineering-based practice in general so we are not the type of architects who work out a design and then ask an engineer to try and make it work. I have always been very keen on engineering and like to feel that I understand quite a lot about it. Not all architects have this belief in the importance of engineering and the importance of what you might call the bones of the building. Some architects think creative engineering design is actually a guy using every ounce of his genius to make something happen that they want to happen. I would put Daniel Libeskind in that bracket but it is not what I would call a collaborative arrangement.'[105]

Nicholas Grimshaw started in architectural practice in 1965 in a partnership with Terry Farrell which lasted until 1980 when they each set up independent practices — Grimshaw founding Nicholas Grimshaw and Partners. As with Foster, Hopkins and, to a lesser extent, Rogers, Grimshaw found that industrial buildings provided a fertile ground for experimentation and the introduction of new technologies into architecture — something that interested him greatly — and the essential characteristics of the work that he did prior to the Waterloo Terminal are to be found in the industrial and commercial buildings that he designed in the 1970s and 1980s.

Grimshaw's buildings belong to the 'rationalist determinist' strand of Modernism in which general arrangement and massing are generated from considerations of function (the programme) and in which the visual vocabulary is celebrative of technology and of the machine. The influences that have operated on him are the same as those that affected his British contemporaries. In the tradition of British Modernism he draws on the ideas of the Arts and Crafts Movement of the late nineteenth century and on the imagery and design methodology that produced the functional buildings of the first industrial revolution. He is particularly interested in the exploitation of new technology and in the opportunities for visual expression that this creates, and he acknowledges[106] a debt to pre-Modern pioneers such as Paxton and Brunel as well as to near contemporaries such as Jean Prouvé, Charles Eames and Richard Buckminster Fuller. Like many contemporary architects he recognises the image-making potential of non-architectural technologies and, in the catalogue of the major exhibition of his work that was shown in London in 1998, he included illustrations of sailing ships, flying machines, motor cars and other artefacts from the world of engineering in a way that recalls Le Corbusier's use of similar images earlier in the century.

Grimshaw applies these ideas in a late twentieth - /early twenty-first century context. In common with most of the generation of architects who entered the profession in the 1960s, he is interested in the relationship between living and working, and believes that the workplace should provide a humane and uplifting environment. The

Fig. 7.1. Herman Miller Factory, Bath, England. Cladding panels are demountable and interchangeable.

Nicholas Grimshaw and Partners.

programmes for his buildings are greatly influenced by social issues. In his Financial Times Printing Works building in London's Docklands, for example, the printing hall, with its massive machines, was made a central feature of the main elevation and given an all-glazed wall. The machine operators, who in most print works are buried in a windowless space deep within the building, were provided with a visual connection with the outside world.

Grimshaw also feels that the users and occupiers of buildings should play some part in the organisation of their environment. He is at pains always to acquire a clear and detailed brief and aims to produce buildings which are sufficiently flexible to allow the users to modify and adapt their environment to suit their changing needs.

This is well illustrated in the Herman Miller Factory building near Bath, England, completed in 1976. Working for a client who was very sympathetic to his design philosophy, Grimshaw created a stylish building that was genuinely flexible in use because the plan could be easily adapted to accommodate changing circumstances. Planning flexibility was provided by the adoption of a relatively long-span structure (to minimise the number of internal columns), the inclusion of a roof services zone and plug-in toilet services and by the development of a cladding system of solid and transparent panels that were genuinely demountable and interchangeable (*Fig. 7.1*).

The key to flexibility in the cladding system was the use of a sub-framework of hollow-section steel columns and rails that was bolted to the primary structure and that coincided with the junctions between the cladding panels. This carried a purpose-designed aluminium extrusion, to which the panels were attached, and which was capable of accepting panel edges of any material up to a thickness of 7 mm (*Fig. 7.2*). Neoprene gaskets made the joints weathertight. Grimshaw worked closely with component manufacturers to develop this system and evolved details that were both practical in use and visually stylish.

Grimshaw's buildings are mostly constructed from the 'new' materials of metal, plastic and glass rather than from masonry or timber. He would argue that this is because these are the best materials for the kinds of buildings that he designs and not out of any notion of wishing to appear modern. The concern has been with the idea of the appropriateness of technology. The steel framework clad in metal and glass is much more adaptable than the 'inflexible extensions to the earth's crust'[107] which result when buildings are made in masonry.

Much of the delight of Grimshaw's architecture is in the visual quality of the detail — the very neat junctions between cladding elements and the exquisitely formed connections between structural elements and at the places where the cladding is fixed to the structure. The buildings are therefore well-crafted assemblies of factory-made components.

'...there are very few universally admired buildings where the detailing is not superb.'[108]

'I get very involved with detail myself. It carries right through to visiting the works, seeing the steelwork being made and then to the erection on site. It's not just an ideas thing. It is a continuum from the very first concept discussions through to the final erection on site.'[109]

The preoccupation has been with making something which works well in every sense and in this respect Grimshaw's attitude to structure and detail is subtly different to that of his mainstream High Tech contemporaries. Whereas architects like Rogers and, to a lesser extent, Foster and Hopkins, have manipulated the imagery of technology for purely visual effect, often compromising its performance in the process, Grimshaw has refined the appearance of that which would perform well. He is concerned with ornamentation of structure rather than with structure as ornament and in this respect remains more faithful to the nineteenth-century origins of this type of architecture in Britain than have his contemporaries.

Grimshaw accords scrupulous respect, during the design process, to the two principal factors which affect the way in which a material can be sensibly used: its physical properties and the available techniques for fashioning it into useful objects. He says:

'It is impossible to design components without understanding the machines on which they are made and the processes they pass through.'[110]

He does not therefore make impossible demands on the people who make his buildings but works with them to evolve solutions that are sensible and practical as well as beautiful — much in the manner of the architects of the Arts and Crafts Movement.

This is not to say that the simplest, most pragmatic structures have always been adopted. In the Sainsbury Supermarket in Camden, London, for example, where something of the feeling of a traditional market hall was evoked, or at the Ice Rink at Oxford (*Fig. 7.3*), where a spectacular masted structure was adopted to convey the excitement of the activity going on within the building, fairly sophisticated structural forms were used. In each case technical issues such as the length of the span and the ground conditions encountered also influenced the choice of structure. In both of these buildings, however, the structure itself and the details of its connections to the building envelope that it supports were not manipulated for stylistic reasons. Once the choice of structure had been made, the main influence on the development of the design was that it should perform well in a technical sense. Structure and detail were enabled to evolve into architecture.

The building which perhaps best exemplifies the approach of Grimshaw in the 1980s is the Financial Times Printing Works (*Figs 7.4* and *7.5*). This has a highly functional rectangular plan with paper reel loading bay and storage at one end and dispatch loading bay at

the other. The central part of this tripartite building consists of the production areas and contains publishing rooms, the plate making room, a workshop, offices and, occupying the whole of one side, the press hall with its large-scale machinery. The sequence of spaces is entirely logical and practical and was determined by the processes that are carried on within the building rather than any considerations of philosophically-based architectural theory. As in most of Grimshaw's buildings, service towers containing stairs and lifts are separate from the main plan and project forward from the face of the building in a clear articulation of served and servant spaces. In this archetypal Grimshaw building, process and a concern for the wellbeing of its users have determined the plan and the general arrangement.

The production areas have all-glass walls and the method by which these are supported allowed Grimshaw ample scope to indulge his passion for good detailing. The most onerous problem was the glass wall of the press hall which spanned 15 m vertically between the ground floor slab and the roof in response to out-of-plane wind loading. The principal elements supporting this glass wall are the main structural columns which hold up the roof. These are encased in metal cladding and serve also as mullions. Lateral loads are conducted to them from the glass through cantilevers attached to the mullions in balanced pairs. In a separate system, the weights of these outriggers and of the glass which they

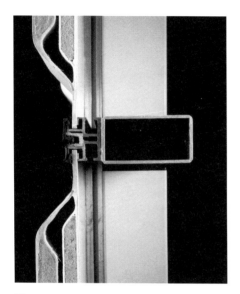

Fig. 7.2. Herman Miller Factory, Bath, England. Detail of attachment of cladding to rolled hollow-section secondary structure.

support are transmitted to the tops of the mullions through a system of tie-rods. This tertiary system of mullions, outriggers and tension rods, together with the cast-steel connectors which link them and the fixings to the glass, provide the observer with a feast of good detailing in metal and glass.

In summary, the principal characteristics of Grimshaw's architecture are, firstly, that logical solutions are sought to the satisfaction of programmatic and technical requirements unaffected by overriding preoccupations with style. Key programmatic considerations are a concern for the quality of life of the occupants and a desire to allow them some capability of modifying their environment. Secondly, building

forms are evolved which are readable and understandable and carefully crafted so that they perform their functions well. Thirdly, great care is taken at all stages of the design process to ensure that visible components, from large-scale structural elements to the smallest fixing screw, are satisfactory visually while at the same time capable of fulfilling their technical role well.

Grimshaw's concern has therefore been with the art of building rather than with building as art. In the 1970s his architecture was more literal than other High Tech architecture: planning was functional and expressed; technology was not compromised. During the 1980s, the growing confidence and skill with the technology seems to have allowed more

Fig. 7.3. Ice Rink, Oxford, England. The visually exciting masted structure was justified by the ground conditions of this relatively long-span structure.

expressive forms to be adopted as, for example, with the Oxford Ice Rink, the Sainsbury Supermarket at Camden, which has been described as 'a hangar crossed with an aircraft carrier',[111] or, more recently, the ship-like Western News building in Plymouth.

Nicholas Grimshaw and Partners.

Fig. 7.4. Financial Times Printing Works, London Docklands, England. The entrance is flanked by expressed stair towers and the all-glass wall of the print hall.

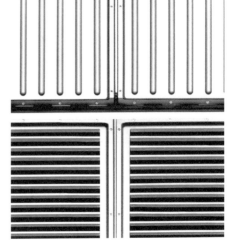

Fig. 7.5. Financial Times Printing Works, London Docklands, England. Detail of the cladding, exemplifying the care which was taken over every aspect of the design.

The International Rail Terminal, Waterloo Station, London

The International Rail Terminal at Waterloo in London (*Fig. 7.6*) is the most significant piece of railway architecture to have been built in Britain since the train sheds of the nineteenth century.[112] British Rail, the client for the project, expressed a wish that the building should be a striking and stylish work of architecture but the brief was, of course, heavily constrained by its function as an international rail terminal. Provision had to be made for the ingress and egress of large numbers of passengers (15 million per year with peak flows of 6000 per hour), and for the accommodation of ticketing, customs, immigration and baggage security facilities as well as a departure lounge with catering facilities, car parking and, of course, the accommodation of state-of-the-art trains 400 m long and carrying 800 passengers each. The brief was complicated by the site, which was long, narrow, tapering and of serpentine shape on plan and bounded on its long sides by the existing Waterloo station on one side and by a public road on the other, both of which would have to remain in use throughout the construction period. The foundation conditions were also less than ideal and included existing brick masonry arches and a road underbridge with both triangulated and plate-girder main elements. The Hunt–Grimshaw combination, with its experience of producing buildings which were capable of satisfying complicated programmatic requirements and that did not compromise important aspects of function for the sake of architectural whim, but which were, nevertheless, striking architecturally, was ideally suited to the satisfaction of this very challenging set of requirements.

The circumstances under which they were commissioned are interesting. Hunt became involved with the project before Grimshaw. British Rail had originally intended that their in-house architects department would carry out the design and Hunt was asked to comment on an early scheme which they had prepared. He recalls[113] that it was overly complex and involved a steel superstructure supported on an array of masts and cables. He was, nevertheless, subsequently invited to act as the structural engineering consultant.

A considerable delay then occurred during which British Rail (BR) decided that an outside firm of architects should be appointed to design the scheme. BR drew up a short list of 12 prominent practices with a view to carrying out a series of competitive interviews before making a final selection. Tony Hunt, who had been retained as a consultant, was asked to comment on the short-listed firms. Norman Foster, Richard Rogers and Nicholas Grimshaw were not on the list and Tony Hunt suggested that they be added to it. BR revealed that it had originally included Foster in the list and that he had stated that he did not wish to become involved due to pressure of other work. BR had consciously excluded Rogers because they did not feel that his type of architecture was appropriate. Tony Hunt's advice to add Grimshaw was accepted and Hunt was therefore instrumental in his eventual appointment.

BR were concerned that the distinguished nineteenth-century tradition of British railway architectural engineering, which had produced train sheds that were both functional and beautiful, should be respected and clearly saw that Grimshaw's approach was the most likely to produce this. The selection panel visited the Financial Times building and were impressed by the heroic feel of the building and, following a competitive interview, Nicholas Grimshaw and Partners were duly appointed as architects for the whole scheme.

The design which they produced envisaged a building that was in two distinct parts: on three levels at and below platform level, a conventional post-and-beam, reinforced-concrete structure was used to accommodate the various passenger handling facilities and car parking; above platform level, an oversailing train shed, consisting of a series of steelwork arches supporting a metal and glass cladding system, provided a spectacular roof for the platforms and tracks. This clear subdivision of elements was the result of a conscious architectural decision to provide a fitting architectural experience. It was recognised that a train shed involving a long-span structure would produce the kind of space which befitted the drama, excitement and romance of an international arrival or departure.[114]

Fig. 7.6. Waterloo International Railway Terminal, London, England.

Photo: J. Reid and J. Peck

Only the train shed part of the building is considered further here. The design of this was a truly collaborative effort between the Hunt and Grimshaw offices. Whereas, in a conventional relationship between architects and engineers, the structure would have been designed by the engineers and the cladding by the architects, probably in conjunction with the manufacturer of the system, at Waterloo the architectural and engineering teams collaborated over all aspects of the building. The Grimshaw team became very much involved with the design of the structure, particularly with the visual aspects of the complicated connections. Hunt's team contributed to the design of the sophisticated cladding system. Architects and engineers therefore worked together to produce a building that worked well both visually and technically.

Due to the awkward geometry of the site (Fig. 7.7), the schemes that were devised for both structure and cladding were very complex. The site had a curvilinear plan which tapered from a width of approximately 50 m at the north (town) end to approximately 33 m at the south (country) end. Within this, five railway tracks and their associated platforms, whose layout was dictated by train operating requirements, had to be accommodated. A particular problem was that one of these tracks had to be placed very close to the western boundary of the site. A total height limit of 15 m was imposed because it was intended that an air-rights building would be constructed above part of the roof as a source of

revenue to fund the project.[115]

Another technical factor which affected the design of both structure and cladding was the need to accommodate three kinds of predicted movement of the various support structures that underpinned the 400 m long building. Firstly, there were differences in the amount of settlement or heave that would occur in the substrata that underlay the building. Secondly, there was the predicted vertical movement that would occur due to the weights of the trains as they moved in and out. Thirdly, loads caused by the acceleration and deceleration of the trains would cause horizontal movement.

The structure which was designed to accommodate these onerous conditions was simple in principle but complex in detail. The basic structural arrangement was conventional, with primary structural elements spanning across the building and carrying secondary elements to which the cladding was attached. A clear span across the entire width of the building was adopted for the primary structure. This not only created a dramatic space, it also meant that no part of the superstructure obstructed the platforms, whose width was critically small due to the narrowness of the site. In view of the spans involved, an arch form was selected for the primary structural elements and, due to the need for clearance for trains on the track that would run adjacent to the western edge of the building, this was given an asymmetrical profile. A discontinuous three-hinge arrangement was

Fig. 7.7. Waterloo International Railway Terminal, London, England. The site has a challenging shape on plan with a tapering curvilinear form.

Photo: Anthony Hunt Associates

129

adopted (*Fig. 7.8*) so that the expected movement of the support structures would be accommodated without the introduction of stress into the steelwork.

The low rise of the arches, which was necessary to comply with the restriction on overall height, meant that a significant level of bending moment was generated under peak loading conditions and a fully-triangulated space truss was adopted to minimise the weight of steel required. The hinge at the apex of the arch was located at the point of contraflexure in the bending-moment diagram and subdivided the arch into two parts of unequal length. The smaller (minor) truss, at the western side, was given a tight-radius curve to provide clearance for the adjacent track. The larger (major) truss at the eastern side had a much larger radius of curvature. Due to the position of the hinge, each truss was subjected entirely to either hogging- or sagging-type bending moment (hogging in the case of the minor truss and sagging for the major truss) so that no reversal of stress occurred in the principal sub-elements: the outer booms of each truss carried either compression or tension with no change of force type along their lengths.

It made sense to attach the secondary structural elements to the compressive booms of the arch trusses so that they provided lateral restraint to inhibit buckling and thus reduce the required member sizes. This meant that the cladding-support system was fixed to the inner boom of the minor trusses and the outer booms

of the major trusses, with the result that the steelwork was outside the cladding on the western side of the building and inside the cladding on the eastern side.

The secondary structure consisted principally of circular hollow-section tube elements spaced at 3·6 m centres spanning between the primary arch elements. The strengths of these were supplemented by tie rods in a semi-trussing arrangement that helped to minimise the sizes required so as not to detract from the visual clarity of the basic structural arrangement. Tension rods were provided above and below those secondary elements which spanned between the major trusses, giving them the ability to resist both an upward and a downward acting load. Space limitations did not permit this arrangement with the minor trusses where tie-rod support was only possible under downward acting load. Uplift had to be resisted solely by the secondary tubes themselves and these were made continuous to reduce the sizes required. The joints between the secondary tubes and the compression booms of the primary structure were welded to provide full continuity and the site joints were made by ingeniously detailed bolted connections at the points of contraflexure of the resulting continuous beam arrangement.

The basic design of the steelwork was therefore fairly straightforward with a logical primary/secondary element arrangement configured to minimise element sizes while at the same time satisfying the various requirements

specific to this particular building. Very great ingenuity and inventiveness were required to realise the design economically on the very difficult curvilinear and tapering site plan without compromising the architectural opportunities which the scheme afforded. It was in the resolution of this potential conflict that the skill and experience of the Hunt–Grimshaw team was particularly effective.

For good structural reasons the arch elements of the primary structure have a fairly complex geometry (*Fig. 7.9*). They are fully three-dimensional space-trusses of triangular cross-section with the principal longitudinal sub-elements (the top and bottom booms) at the apices of the triangle. In profile, the depths vary to correspond approximately with the bending-moment diagrams and they are lozenge-shaped in plan, giving an overall three-dimensional form similar to that of a banana.

Two significant problems arose in connection with the fabrication of the trusses: firstly, that of devising an economical way of coping with the variations in span and height that occurred due to the tapering, curvilinear form of the plan, and secondly, of detailing the many complex three-dimensional joints that were involved. The first of these required that some form of standardisation be incorporated to prevent the scheme from becoming totally uneconomic. The manner in which this was achieved was little short of brilliant.

The span of the primary trusses reduces

from 48·5 m to 32·7 m in 16 steps and the overall height of the roof and the truss depths and widths were scaled down in proportion to the reduction in span. By keeping some dimensions constant for all trusses (for example, the difference in level between the foundation hinges) and scaling down all others, the geometry at most connections remained constant for all trusses — only the lengths of the sub-elements were different. Variations in the diameters of the sub-elements were limited to two and this meant that only two different patterns were required for each

nodal connection. A remarkable degree of standardisation was therefore achieved and this allowed the cost of fabrication to be contained within acceptable limits. It also meant that all trusses were of similar appearance and disguised the fact that changes in the sizes of the trusses occur, in steps. The finished building appears to diminish in size continuously with no awkward discontinuities and this is a very important element of its visual quality. This aspect of the design illustrates well the level of commitment that the architects and engineers brought to the

Fig. 7.9. Waterloo International Railway Terminal, London, England. Space trusses of the main elements have a complex banana-shaped geometry.

Fig. 7.8. Waterloo International Railway Terminal, London, England. Cross-section. The primary structural elements are space frames in a three-hinge arrangement. The asymmetry was necessary due to the proximity of the westernmost track to the edge of the building. The designers were given no flexibility in the layout of the tracks.

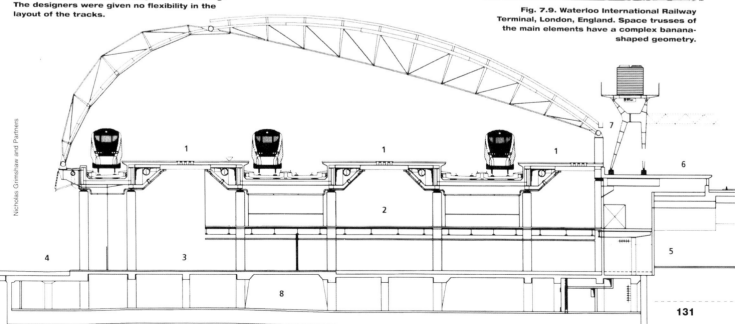

project. That they were able to devise an overall form which appeared to be a continuously diminishing tube but which could also be constructed economically says much for their skill and ingenuity.

The key to the problem of achieving complex three-dimensional joints that were visually satisfying was the use of cast steel nodes (*Figs 7.10* to *7.12*). The Hunt office was by this time familiar with this technology, as they had been involved with it since the INMOS project of nearly a decade earlier. The very large nodes that were required at the two foundation hinges and at the apex hinge of each arch were refined to a form that was both elegant and expressive of the structural action. The most complex connections occurred on the tension sides of the main trusses where up to five elements and a further three tie-rods, associated with the secondary structure, came together at each node. The use of cast nodes allowed a simplicity of form which would have been impossible with conventional welded and/or bolted connections.

A further difficulty was presented by the difference in the sizes of the compression and tension sides of the structure. The compression booms of the arches were circular hollow-section tubes of 355 mm diameter at the mid-span location reducing in size to 219 mm in diameter at the ends. The changes in diameter were accommodated by the use of capping plates at the butt joints between the sub-elements. The tension booms were of 75 mm diameter solid rod. In the interest of minimising the sizes of the complicated

connections on the tension side of the structure it was necessary to keep the sizes of the elements as small as possible. This meant that the main scantling elements that separated the compressive and tension booms had to be tapered so that they could make satisfactory joints with the large-diameter tubes on the compression side at one end and with small-diameter rods on the tension side at the other. The tapered elements were fashioned by a technique that had been developed previously by YRM Anthony Hunt Associates: trapezoidal plates were bent in a large brake press to form half cones which were welded together to form the conically-shaped tapered scantlings (*Fig. 7.13*). The final forms of all of the connections in the primary trusses were developed and refined by CAD techniques and in consultation with Nicholas Grimshaw and Partners. The criteria applied were that the forms would perform well from both a structural and an aesthetic viewpoint, these two requirements being accorded equal status.

A third problem, solved in conjunction with the cladding subcontractor, was to devise the complexly-shaped cladding envelope without the need for large numbers of differently-shaped or even uniquely-shaped cladding panels. The all-glass western wall where the cladding support rails and brackets were prominently visible presented a particularly difficult design challenge. The Hunt and Grimshaw teams acting, with Briggs Amasco Curtain Wall Ltd. jointly developed a system of extruded aluminium

Fig. 7.10. Waterloo International Railway Terminal, London, England. A partially completed cast-steel node of the primary structure.

glazing bars and stainless steel brackets which formed an interface between the steelwork structure and the glazing itself. This allowed the complex surface to be covered by a series of identical rectangular glass panels, each with an aluminium frame around its perimeter.

The glazing bars were bolted to the secondary elements of the main structure through cranked cast stainless steel rocking brackets (*Fig. 7.14*). The crank angle was adjustable during the assembly of the roof, to accommodate construction tolerances and variations in the truss geometry between panels, and were locked up finally by a clamping bolt once the assembly was complete. Each bracket was then free to rotate about its attachment to the main structure, in order to permit movement caused by temperature changes and by the live-load deflection of the support structure. The edge junctions between the glass panels were sealed with concertina neoprene gaskets which accommodated variations in the gaps between them caused by the complexity of the overall form. The whole assembly was a *tour-de-force* of detailing that represented the culmination of a design philosophy that was central to the ethos of both the Grimshaw and the Hunt offices. Every component of the system had a shape that was both functional and elegant and the whole design

Fig. 7.12. Waterloo International Railway Terminal, London, England. Cast-steel nodes are seen here on the tension side of the structure allowing the creation of neat joints of complex shape. The tapered scantlings are also visible.

Fig. 7.11. Waterloo International Railway Terminal, London, England. The cast-steel nodes were welded to the sub-elements of the structure to produce joints that were visually satisfactory despite being of complex geometry.

was an object lesson in the creation of solutions that satisfy technical and aesthetic requirements in equal measure.

The Waterloo Terminal, taken as a whole, is the type of architecture at which the Grimshaw office excels. The clear programmatic requirements and functional tradition of railway architecture lend themselves to the Grimshaw approach and a railway terminal was created that was not only functional but which contained spaces at all levels that were both architecturally exciting and enjoyable in use. The railway passenger, who may use the building occasionally,

Photo: Anthony Hunt Associates

Photo: J Reid and J. Peck

and the staff, who are there every day, are provided with an experience which enhances their lives.

The building is particularly remarkable for the elegance with which a high degree of standardisation was achieved in the fabrication of the highly complex geometry of the train shed, resulting in an enclosure that was economical, practical and of high architectural quality. The use of state-of-the-art technology — in particular in the casting of steel and the development of the design through CAD techniques — was also notable.

The building is a genuinely high tech affair. At Waterloo the frontiers of what was buildable were approached, and, as is always

Fig. 7.13. Waterloo International Railway Terminal, London, England. The tapered scantlings which link the tension and compression sides of the primary frames were manufactured from flat plate. Trapezoidal plates were bent into half cones which were then welded together.

Fig. 7.14. Waterloo International Railway Terminal, London, England. Cladding bracket linking the cladding-support structure to the main framework. The crank angle was adjustable to facilitate assembly. Once in position the mid-joint was locked up so that the crank angle was fixed. The bracket, as a whole, could still rotate about the central joint to accomodate movement of the frame in service.

the case when the limits of what is technically feasible are encountered, truly high tech solutions were required. Unlike many of its near contemporaries to which the label High Tech is applied, the Waterloo Terminal can stand comparison with such iconic buildings as the Crystal Palace and the train sheds of the nineteenth century as a genuine example of the appropriate use of state-of-the-art technology in the creation of architectural form.

The description of the building given here has concentrated on the train shed, which represents only 10% of the total cost of the project. It is, nevertheless, the part of the building in which the most dramatic combination of architecture and engineering occurs and therefore the part most noticed by users and commentators alike. It is a fitting testament to the combined talents and skills of the Grimshaw and Hunt offices.

Grimshaw and Hunt

The Waterloo Terminal was to be the first of a number of buildings carried out by the Hunt and Grimshaw offices in the 1990s and beyond. Notable projects are the Combined Operations Centre for British Airways at Heathrow Airport, London and the Eden Project in Cornwall. The latter, especially, which is a series of greenhouses formed by interconnected lattice domes of very complex geometry, provided the kind of challenge that was so successfully met at Waterloo. It is to be regretted, however, that Hunt and Grimshaw did not work together in the 1970s and 80s when the type of architecture at which they excel was pioneered in Britain. Of all the architects who were practising in this period, Grimshaw was the one who had the greatest understanding of technical issues and therefore of what Tony Hunt had to offer.

Chapter Eight
The engineer's contribution to architecture

Chapter Eight
The engineer's contribution to architecture

Introduction

There have been three aspects to Tony Hunt's success as a leading engineer of his generation. Firstly, there is the quality of his engineering: he has designed structures which are not only visually exciting, but which stand up well to purely technical criticism. The integrity of his structures has never been compromised for visual effect. As works of engineering, judged by technical criteria, they stand comparison with those of the great exemplars, such as Brunel, Eiffel and Maillart.

Secondly, there has been Tony Hunt's ability to work in a collaborative way with both engineering colleagues and with architects. Teamwork is very much the ethos at Anthony Hunt Associates and Hunt has employed this methodology from the very beginning of his career and from the earliest of his collaborative relationships with architects. He possesses many of the basic skills of the architect, ranging from an easy free-hand drafting technique to an eye for form and proportion. Architects have known that if Hunt were involved there would be no conflict between the architectural and the engineering objectives because their own concerns were also his concerns. A consequence of this has been that engineering issues could be accorded a high place in the architectural agenda. Tony Hunt is one of the handful of engineers who has earned engineering a place at the top table — the place where the basic architectural decisions are made. In the broad context of the history of twentieth-century architecture, this has perhaps been his greatest achievement.

Thirdly, as Ove Arup and Felix Samuely had done earlier, Hunt established one of the leading engineering consultancies of the late twentieth century — a place in which the brightest young engineers were nurtured and to which they were attracted. He is, on one level, a good businessman, capable of holding together a successful firm, and on another, an enlightened, inspiring and congenial employer, who has created a stimulating environment in which high quality work has been appreciated.

The aesthetics of structure and its relationship to engineering

Tony Hunt was able to win the confidence of the architects with whom he worked because he was concerned that structures should be elegant as well as useful. This places him in the company of the important architect/engineers of the twentieth century, such as Nervi, Torroja, Morandi and Candela and raises the difficult question of the aesthetics of engineering. What is elegance, in this context? How is it accomplished in Modern structural technology and what has been the contribution of Tony Hunt to its articulation in relation to that of his contemporaries?

A study of the structures produced by Tony Hunt and his colleagues at AHA provides some of the answers to these questions. It is worth noting that they have been devised in the context of buildings whose forms have been determined by design teams of which they were a part. This distinguishes them from architect/engineers such as Torroja or Nervi who were able to exercise full control so far as the creation of structural form was concerned. That Hunt and his team were able to produce structures that performed well both visually and technically, in contexts where structural performance was only one of several factors influencing the design, says much for their skill both as engineers and as communicators, and for their commitment to the visual aspects of design. Hunt and his colleagues accommodate the ideas of their architectural collaborators. They produce structures in which the aesthetic and technical agendas are reconciled. This cannot always be said with such confidence of their contemporaries. The aspects of their structures that are the most significant are *refinement of appearance*, *appropriateness* and *readability*.

Refinement of appearance

Tony Hunt and AHA have been pioneers in the UK of the elegant exposed steel framework. Crucial factors were the adoption of forms which minimised the magnitudes of internal forces, and therefore allowed slender elements to be specified, and the evolution of joint details which performed well visually as well as technically. Hunt became interested in the visual qualities of steelwork at the very beginning of his career, while working with Samuely, and later brought about a revolution in this aspect of structural design.

When Hunt set up his practice in the early 1960s the standard connection methods for steelwork elements in architectural structures were riveting or bolting. Both involved the extensive use of gusset plates, angle cleats and other jointing components because the load-carrying capacities of individual bolts or rivets were relatively low and large numbers were required. As a consequence, gusset plates and other jointing components tended to be large in order to provide extensive areas of overlap between the elements being connected.

Joints in steelwork were clumsy and ugly. This was of no particular consequence because, prior to the 1960s, steelwork was rarely visible in buildings which were considered worthy to be termed architecture[116] because it was concealed under fireproofing material. The structural engineering consultant for a building would normally specify only the element sizes for a steel framework, leaving the design of the connections entirely to the fabricator. Exposed steelwork, with cumbersome riveted connections, was commonly used for industrial buildings but these were regarded as the vernacular rather than as architecture.

Tony Hunt and the architects with whom he worked were responsible for the introduction of elegant exposed steelwork to British architecture. This was greatly dependent on two technical advances: welded and cast-steel connections, particularly cast-steel connections that could also be welded. Both of these advances

were in turn dependent upon the existence of suitable steels and so it is perhaps worth mentioning here that the unsung heroes of this story are the metallurgists who developed, firstly, rolled steels and then cast steels which could be welded. As has often been the case in the history of Western architecture, the emergence of the new in visual terms was dependent upon technological advances. The people of vision who created the new architecture were to a large extent exploiting a new technology and in the process extending the boundaries of what was possible architecturally.

The process of welding, in which the edges of two metal components are heated until liquid with the addition of some extra molten metal of identical composition, so that they flow together, is the most effective way of making a structural connection between two pieces of steel. The weld forms a solid metal junction between the components being joined and, in effect, unites them into a single component with no discontinuity between the original parts. In welded joints there are no concentrations of stress such as occur in bolted connections, and a junction is created which is more effective structurally and neater visually than can be obtained with mechanical fasteners such as bolts or rivets. Welding can be problematic, however, because the properties of steel are affected by the rate at which it cools from the molten state. If this occurs too quickly, the metal can become brittle and the process of welding can have a detrimental effect on the properties of the steel adjacent to the connections, with potentially disastrous consequences.

Modern welding techniques evolved from the early twentieth century onwards and the associated problems had largely been solved by the early 1960s, by which time welding was a well-established technique in industry, especially shipbuilding, but such was the conservative nature of the world of building construction, that it was virtually unknown in the field of architecture.

The architectural use of the exposed, welded-steel framework was pioneered in Britain by Hunt, Foster and Rogers. Reliance Controls was perhaps the seminal building. The Hunstanton School was the first significant building in Britain to have an exposed steel structure but this was crude, no doubt intentionally, by comparison. What made the Reliance Controls building special was the high degree of refinement of the welded structure. The building received favourable criticism and drew attention to the aesthetic possibilities of welded steel. It initiated a fresh interest in the ornamental use of steel structure in Britain and provided great stimulus for the widespread adoption of welding for architectural structures.

Another important feature of the Reliance Controls building was that the welding was carried out on site (*Fig. 8.1*). In the 1960s welding of steel was regarded, in the building industry, as a new technology to be conducted only in the controlled environment of the factory. Welded-steel structures were therefore prefabricated by factory welding into components that were small enough to be transported and were detailed in such a way that the site connections were made by bolting. The Reliance Controls building demonstrated that, although welding on site was more tricky than bolting, it was a feasible procedure. This extended the architectural possibilities of the steel structure.

Throughout the 1970s, Tony Hunt and AHA continued to exploit the opportunities offered by welding to produce structures with clean lines, neat connections and slender elements. Other engineers began doing the same as the High Tech movement gathered momentum in the 1970s. By the 1980s the well-crafted, exposed steelwork structure was well-established. In almost all cases such structures were based on simple post-and-beam forms. More complex structures, based on mast-and-cable support systems, were also being investigated as a means of economically achieving long spans and column-free interiors. Two prominent examples were the Fleetguard Manufacturing and Distribution Centre at Quimper, in Brittany, France by Richard Rogers and Partners and the Ice Rink at Oxford, in England (*Fig. 7.3*), by Nicholas Grimshaw and Partners, both of which were engineered by Ove Arup and Partners. These masted structures tended to have more complex, multi-element joints than were required for post-and-beam frameworks, and they stretched to the

Fig. 8.1. Reliance Controls building, Swindon, England. Site welding of the structure. Team 4, 1966.

Photo: Anthony Hunt Associates

limit the possibilities of achieving tidy connections with welding. The difficulties of making suitable connections did in fact place a restriction on the complexity of form that was possible in this genre. The development that would allow complex three-dimensional arrangements to be created without compromising the appearance of structures was the cast-steel node.

Casting of ferrous metal for structural purposes fell out of use in the late nineteenth century following problems associated with the brittleness of cast iron. By the twentieth century, steel, in the form of hot-rolled sections, had superseded iron as the material used for metal structures, and these were usually connected by riveting. Casting of steel for architectural structures was virtually unknown in the first half of the twentieth century. By the middle of the century, cast steel was a well-developed technology in the field of mechanical engineering for the production of components of complex shape for machinery, particularly engine components for ships, locomotives and other types of vehicle. Cast steel was less ductile than rolled steel but the problem of brittle fracture was gradually overcome and the development of techniques such as X-ray and ultrasonic testing allowed the soundness of castings to be proven.

Despite the existence of this technology of cast steel in mechanical engineering, the use of casting in structural steelwork for buildings remained unusual. A rare exception was the cast-steel node of the MERO space frame system, which was developed in the 1940s, but this was a mass-produced manufactured product and subject to the regimes of quality control that were found in the world of mechanical engineering. In the 1960s, when engineers like Hunt started in practice, the use of castings for structural steelwork was virtually unknown.

The reintroduction of casting as a technology for architectural structures occurred in spectacular fashion at the Centre Pompidou in Paris (by Piano and Rogers with Ove Arup and Partners as engineers). The cast-steel 'Gerberettes'[117] (Fig. 8.2) which were used in the Centre Pompidou in the early 1970s, and which formed very prominent elements in its visual vocabulary, were landmarks in the history of steel construction. Casting was the only economical way of making components of such a complex shape. The alternative would have been to machine them from solid blocks of metal, and, given the numbers involved, this would have been prohibitively expensive. Fabrication from rolled components by welding would have been less efficient because much simpler geometries would have had to be adopted. According to Richard Rogers the decision to use cast steel was taken on economic grounds:

'We started Beaubourg with the idea of using off-the-peg components, as at Reliance Controls, but it became obvious that it would not be economic. We were repeating the Gerberette brackets over 200 times and it was cheaper to use less steel than it was to use an I-beam. That's the argument on that I would have thought.'[118]

Necessity was therefore the mother of invention and resulted in the importation into architecture of a technology which was well-tried in other fields. It was, nevertheless, a courageous decision to use something that was so little known in the construction industry.

The cast-steel Gerberettes of the Centre Pompidou were transitional. They were entirely self-contained units connected to the rest of the structure through direct bearing on bolts and pins.

Fig. 8.2. Centre Pompidou, Paris, France. Gerberette bracket. Piano and Rogers, 1978.

The breakthrough that led to the more widespread use of casting was the development of steels that were suitable for both casting and welding. Weldable cast steel allowed simple and neat connecting nodes to be manufactured for complex three-dimensional structures.

Tony Hunt was one of the engineers who pioneered the use of weldable cast steel for the manufacture of joints for complex three-dimensional frameworks. His first uses of this type of cast steel were in the INMOS building in 1982 and his hinge connections of the framework of the Patera building. These formed a prelude to the types of structure in which the technology of casting was exploited to the full: the complex geometry of the train shed of the Waterloo Terminal is an example.

Chapter Eight
The engineer's contribution to architecture

Refinement of the appearance of exposed steel structures has been one of Tony Hunt's major contributions to late twentieth-century architecture. Given that structural steelwork always consists of an assemblage of prefabricated components, the development of elegant ways of joining these together was crucial. His exploitation of the technologies of welding and of cast-steel joints were an important part of this.

Appropriateness

A structure designed by Tony Hunt or AHA may be appreciated on several different levels, the most basic of which is simply as a piece of technology. It will always be found to be appropriately engineered and frequently it will be seen also to contain features that represent clever and elegant solutions to problems set up by architectural requirements. The structural action is never inappropriately fudged to meet constraints imposed by these. Hunt either finds a solution to the problem which is appropriate from a structural viewpoint or works with the architect to modify the building's agenda.

Well-designed structures achieve an appropriate level of efficiency in the use of material. They are also no more complex to design and construct than is necessary. The requirements for efficiency and simplicity often conflict, and one of the tests of good engineering is the manner in which this conflict has been resolved.

It is a truism of structural behaviour that greater complexity is required to achieve higher efficiency in the use of material. A beam with an I-shaped cross-section is more efficient than one with a solid rectangular cross-section; the triangulated girder is more efficient than the solid-web beam; the arch and cable net are more efficient than the straight beam. The level of efficiency which is possible depends therefore on the type of structure involved: the more complex the arrangement the greater is the possible level of efficiency. The disadvantage of complex form is that it is more difficult and therefore more expensive to design, construct and maintain.

The objective of good structural design is not to achieve the highest possible level of efficiency in the use of material, but rather to find an appropriate balance between efficiency and complexity which represents the best economy of means. One of the factors which determines the most appropriate choice of structure for a particular situation is the size of the span. For any particular type of structure, the level of efficiency tends to diminish as the span increases: if a particular level of efficiency is appropriate, progressively more efficient types of structure will be required to achieve it as the span increases. Thus, while an appropriate level of efficiency might be achieved in a short-span structure with a beam of I-shaped cross-section, a triangulated girder might be required to achieve the same level of efficiency over a slightly larger span and a complex space truss or vaulted structure for a still

larger span. For this reason, the longer the span the greater is the justification for the adoption of a complex form.[119]

Examination of structures by Tony Hunt and AHA shows that the choice of structure type is always appropriate. Where short spans have been involved, as at IBM Cosham or the Hopkins House, simple post-and-beam forms were adopted. At intermediate spans, such as Modern Art Glass, the more sophisticated portal frame was used. At the Waterloo Terminal, very complicated space trusses, in arched form, were used. Where the logical selection of form has been departed from, the most prominent example being at the Sainsbury Centre, in which the span justified a portal frame or arched form rather than simple post-and-beam, there were good architectural reasons for its selection and clever devices were adopted to circumvent the consequences of the less-than-ideal basic structural form.

The types of element which have been selected in Tony Hunt's structures have also been compatible with the structural circumstances. Standard rolled I-sections were used for the relatively short spans of the Reliance Controls building. Triangulated sections were used for the shorter spans at IBM Cosham and the Hopkins House but were justified in these cases in the interests of producing lightweight components that could be easily assembled on site. The same was true for the Patera building. The triangulated configurations of the Sainsbury Centre or of

Waterloo Terminal were entirely justified by the spans involved.

Another aspect of appropriateness which is seen in many of Tony Hunt's structures is the use of clever engineering devices to control the behaviour of the structure. The choice of location of the hinge connections in the Sainsbury Centre to redistribute internal forces away from the beam-to-column joint has already been mentioned. Another example, from the Hopkins House, is the use of diagonal and diaphragm vertical-plane bracing which allowed very slender columns to be specified. The composite metal and wood decks which minimised the total depth of decking required in the same structure is another. The hybrid central hinge of the Patera building, which maintained a state of compression in the laterally-restrained inner booms of the trusses under all conditions of load, is yet another. These are devices which make the structures perform better and which allow the adoption of slender elements with small cross-sections. They are demonstrations of the subtleties of engineering technique in the service of architecture — something in which Tony Hunt and his office excel.

One of the most enjoyable aspects of Hunt's structures from a purely engineering point of view is the complete absence of features which are inappropriate structurally and incorporated into the structure solely for dramatic effect. The latter has been a feature of the work of many of his contemporaries, often to the detriment of engineering performance. Much of the work of the Spanish architect/engineer Santiago Calatrava, for example, exciting though it is in visual terms, falls into this category. It is also present in many high tech buildings. The configuration of the Gerberettes at the Centre Pompidou, for example (by Piano and Rogers with Ove Arup and Partners), which sends 25% more load down the columns than is necessary to support the weights of the floors, can hardly be considered desirable from an engineering viewpoint. Nor can the excessively complicated arrangements of masts and tie rods that occur in Foster's Renault Warehouse in Swindon (also with Arups as engineers), unjustified as they are by the span involved.

Tony Hunt does not belong to this virtuosic, 'structural gymnastics', 'make-it-look-impossible' school of engineering. There are no gimmicks in his structures, which fall into the category of ornamentation of structure rather than structure as ornament. Where compromises have been made for visual effect, these have normally been of a minor nature — e.g. use of Universal Column sections for secondary elements in the Reliance Controls building and the redundant bracing in the same building.

The selection of materials is another aspect of Hunt's structures which is always entirely appropriate both visually and in engineering terms, given the spans and loads involved. The majority of his structures in the early years were for single-storey, or at least low-rise, buildings which, by their nature, are subjected to relatively small amounts of imposed load. Frequently, there was also a need to erect the building very quickly. Steel was undoubtedly the most sensible choice of structural material in all of these cases. Where a multi-storey structure of complex form was involved, such as with the Willis, Faber and Dumas building or the Museum of Scotland, reinforced concrete was used as the principal structural material. Again, this was an entirely appropriate choice.

Readability

A distinctive characteristic of Tony Hunt's and AHA's structures is the absence of ambiguity of function. The action of the structure is always clear and there is never any direct conflict between the architectural and the structural idea. This has been the case from the earliest projects onwards. In every case the elevations of the building are almost a diagram of the structure.

In this respect Tony Hunt stands out from his contemporaries. A prominent example of a clash between structure and architecture occurs in the Lloyd's Headquarters building in London by Rogers (Fig. 8.3), for which the engineers were a team from Ove Arup and Partners led by Peter Rice. The structure of the Lloyd's building consists of a series of beam-and-column frames set parallel to each other with reinforced-concrete floors spanning one way between.

The structure of the building is exposed, in accordance with Rogers' idea that buildings should be 'readable' and that the action of the structure would be 'honestly' expressed. In the words of one well known critic, 'the honest expression of materials is an article of faith in this kind of architecture'.[120] Although this condition includes other aspects of materials than their appropriate use structurally, it does imply that the latter should be well resolved. The materials here may be honestly expressed but the structure is not.

In fact, the visible underside of the floor of the Lloyd's building consists of a square grid of small-scale structural ribs which is continuous around the entire doughnut shape of the plan and is not interrupted by the primary-beam elements whose existence is entirely suppressed. The impression given is that the floor structure is a two-way-spanning slab with a square grid of down-stand ribs supported directly on the columns with no primary-beam elements being involved. This is misleading. The suppression of the structural action was carried out entirely for visual reasons and the critical comment quoted above incorrectly assesses the situation.

The engineers of this structure were fully aware of the architectural priorities:

There were particular architectural requirements for the floor structure:

1. The structure should be isotropic in appearance (author's emphasis). It was important that the floor should be seen as a ring rather than two linked rectangles.

Fig. 8.3. Lloyd's Headquarters building, London, England. Richard Rogers and Partners, 1986.

2.The beams should have parallel sides and sharp arrises so the eye would be drawn to the soffit rather than up into the coffer.[121]

The engineers had to exercise great ingenuity to reconcile these visual requirements with those of technical performance.

The nearest that Tony Hunt has come to this kind of compromise was at the Sainsbury Centre where, as is outlined in chapter 4, the arrangement is far from ideal from a structural point of view. The form of the structure is, nevertheless, genuinely (honestly) expressed in the end elevation of the building and is not made to appear to be that which it is not.

The design team

Tony Hunt has made a significant contribution to the establishment of the engineer as a full contributor to the team of designers responsible for determining the aesthetics of buildings. This contribution must be placed in the context of the types of working relationships which are possible between architects and engineers; there has been a wide range of these in the history of western architecture.

At one extreme it is possible for an engineer to act simply as a facilitator, the person who works out how to make a building whose form and general arrangement have been determined entirely by someone else. At the other extreme an engineer may act as the sole designer of a building. Mid-way between these extremes is a situation in which architect and engineer

Fig. 8.4. Plan and elevation of the Villa Emo, Fanzolo, Italy. (Illustration from Palladio, *Quattro Libri dell' Architettura*, 1570). The plans of Palladio's buildings were ideally suited to construction in loadbearing masonry but the architectural interest lay elsewhere.

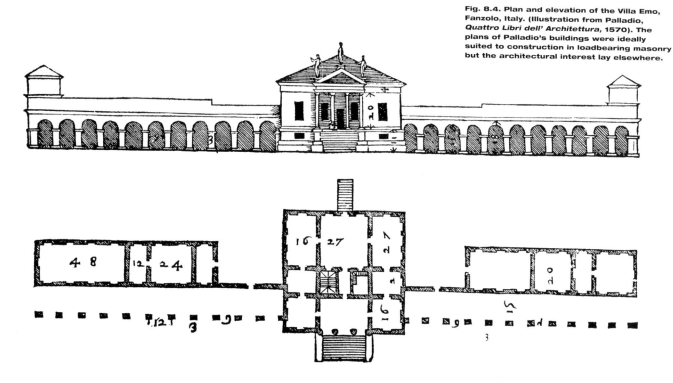

collaborate as equal partners in a design team. This last is the type of relationship favoured by Tony Hunt and AHA. It is a method which is capable of producing buildings which satisfy all of the criteria by which good architecture and good engineering are judged.

The full and equal collaboration between architects and technologists in the determination of the architectural treatment of a building has been a relatively recent phenomenon. From the time of the Italian Renaissance until the Modern period the relationship that existed between architects and those who attended to the technical aspects of building was not a partnership of equals. This was to a large extent due to the fact that most post-Medieval buildings were very unambitious structurally. A technology of masonry walls and timber floor and roof structures was employed, the capabilities of which were well understood and which presented little challenge to the builders. There were obvious exceptions, Brunelleschi's great dome in Florence for example, but in the majority of buildings there was no sense of excitement in relation to the structural make-up. The work of Andrea Palladio may serve as an example. Palladio, who began his working life as a stonemason and who was therefore entirely comfortable with the technology at his disposal, designed buildings which were practical and sensible from a structural viewpoint (*Fig. 8.4*). Their architectural interest, however, depended on the idea of the building as a microcosm and on Palladio's use of harmonic proportion, hierarchical

arrangements of space and innovative uses of classical forms of ornamentation. The means by which the buildings were constructed were of little relevance to this agenda and such was the case with virtually all Renaissance and post-Renaissance buildings. A consequence of this was that structural considerations disappeared from any discussion of architecture.

And so began a long period in which the structures of buildings, and with them the people who were skilled in their design and construction, gradually became distanced from the architectural discourse and the architectural design process. The structure was still present — the building would not stand without it — but it had disappeared from view, both literally, behind a stucco and plaster skin that enveloped the buildings of Europe from the fifteenth century until the nineteenth century, and also metaphorically.

The re-emergence of the structure as a visible contributor to architecture, and with that the re-establishment of the builder and, in the Modern period, the structural engineer, as a contributor to the architectural design process, began with the iron-and-glass structures of the nineteenth century. These buildings were designed by structural engineers who were indifferent to the 'battle of the styles' raging around them in the nineteenth-century world of architecture and who erected buildings that were straightforward technical solutions, unencumbered by stylistic architectural baggage,

to the problems posed by programmatic requirements. They had a refreshing and noble simplicity and a spectacular architectural presence. Their architectural qualities went largely unrecognised at the time, however.

It was not until the twentieth century, when architects once again became interested in tectonics (the making of architecture out of those fundamental parts of a building responsible for holding it up) and in the aesthetic possibilities of the new structural technologies of steel and reinforced concrete, that the architectural qualities of the buildings created by nineteenth-century engineers such as Brunel, Paxton and Barlow were acknowledged. This process brought with it the reappearance, in the architectural mainstream, of the ornamental use of exposed structure which made its tentative first appearance in the works of early Modernists such as Auguste Perret and Peter Behrens and was strongly represented in the later architecture of Walter Gropius, Le Corbusier and Ludwig Mies van der Rohe.

The re-emergence of the exposed structure brought about a gradual shift in the relationship between architects and engineers. Inevitably, in the early period of Modernism the *status quo* was maintained and the design of a building was very much dominated by the architect as the leader of the group of professionals who collaborated over its production. Modernism espoused rationalism but carried with it much of the baggage of nineteenth-century Romanticism. One particularly strong aspect of this situation was the idea of the architect as an heroic figure — in the parlance of architectural criticism, the 'Modern Master'. Thus, although architecture became ever more dependent upon new structural technologies and therefore upon the skill and expertise of engineers, most architects continued to behave, as they had done in the pre-Modern period, as the masters of the design process and to treat the other designers involved as mere technicians. This view was endorsed by most of the critics and historians of Modernism who paid little regard to the technology which underpinned the Modern aesthetic and gave scant acknowledgement to the engineers who developed it.

This situation changed as Modern architecture developed, firstly, with the emergence of the architect/engineers (Pier Luigi Nervi, Eduardo Torroja, Ricardo Morandi, Owen Williams, and, in more recent times, Felix Candela and Santiago Calatrava). These were all individuals from a technical background who produced buildings of architectural quality. They have enjoyed the same kind of status as the leading architects of their day and their work has been considered worthy of review in the architectural media.

That the buildings of the architect/engineers were accepted by the world of architecture and reviewed in the architectural media, which those of their nineteenth-century predecessors had not been, was an indication that the architectural agenda was changing. The

tectonic building, in which the structural armature became an important visual element, had once again become fashionable and the architectural world had once again become interested in exposed structure, possibly for the first time since the Gothic period.

But the gap between architects and engineers was not closed by these engineers who operated as architects. They were part of the existing way of working. The new working practices which led to High Tech, in which engineers and architects collaborated to determine the form of a building, would be developed by the next generation following its tentative beginning in the 1930s with Arup, Samuely and Williams. Tony Hunt belongs to the small group of structural engineers, which included Peter Rice, Ted Happold and Frank Newby, who helped to bring this newer situation into being.

The emergence of the design-team method of working, in which groups of designers come together in a spirit of equality and who each bring a particular skill to the design process, may have been inevitable in the Modern context, but certain architects clearly played key roles in enabling it to happen. The recollections of some of the leading figures involved make an interesting comparison. Norman Foster appears to believe not only that the design methodology adopted by Team 4 was new but also that it was mostly a consequence of his own ideas:

'That is an approach that I pioneered — the bringing together of a group with a shared sense of

enthusiasm and, in a way, to create the environment for individuals from different professional backgrounds to freely contribute, rather than work in a way that they had been educated, [which was] to wait for the architect to say what direction the project was going to take and then deliver accordingly. I think this was a conscious way for me of breaking down barriers and reversing the way in which the professions concerned with construction had been brought up and conditioned. Getting them to interact around a table was the best way of achieving that.'[122]

Even in his student days Foster had advocated this working methodology. He recalls:

'As a student, I did exactly the same thing on a project in the Masters class at Yale which, as I think about it, broke completely new ground. At that time, or indeed at any time, nobody had ever suggested that it would be helpful to have an engineer in the studio and nobody else wanted to talk to an engineer. I remember very clearly saying that I wanted to be able to sit down and discuss the product with an engineer.'[123]

The role of Richard Rogers was also significant. He recalls:

'I remember very well talking to Norman [Foster] and saying, we are not going to build like Jim Stirling — we do not want to build the way he does, which is basically to solve the engineering problem afterwards.'[124]

Other architects were also interested in this method of working. Nicholas Grimshaw attempted, from the beginning, to establish close working relationships with structural engineers:

'I think we are a very engineering-based practice in general, so we are not the type of architects who work out a design and then ask an engineer to try and make it work. We have never been like that. I do believe in long design sessions with everyone sitting round the table throwing ideas into the ring and fighting for them.'[125]

An interesting aspect of Foster's account of the development of the design-team methodology is his recollection of the mild hostility that some of his collaborators had to this method of working. He says:

'It was not without its frustrations, in the sense that I would recall the occasional complaint of: why are we all sitting here and we have not got a design yet?'[126]

The feelings of the engineers who took this view may perhaps be appreciated. They were used to being presented with a finished design into which they inserted a structure and may have felt that their time was being wasted in the discursive design meetings with architects in which the forms of buildings were evolved. Foster's comment gives an indication of the novelty of the method of working. Tony Hunt was a willing collaborator in its introduction. Foster, describing design meetings in the early days of the Reliance Controls building, said:

'Tony Hunt would be, as it were, emptying the trash can of all the conventional structures that might be associated with a factory.'[127]

This conjures up a vision of someone who was excited by the discursive process for evolving a design. It raises the issue of the significance of engineers to its introduction. The views of the architects vary. While all who worked with Tony Hunt acknowledge the unique qualities that he brought to the design process, they differ in their assessment of whether or not the design-team methodology could have emerged independently of figures like Hunt, Happold and Rice. Rogers is quite clear that they could not. Asked how many engineers could work successfully in this way he responded:

'I would be hard pressed to find half a dozen that I have met in my thirty-something years in practice. There is Tony Hunt, Peter Rice, Frank Newby, Chris Wise ... there are very few.'[128]

Foster and Grimshaw take a different view. Foster says:

'We have worked with an extraordinary number of engineers and as a generalisation I would say that, if somebody is well schooled in structural engineering ... that given the creation of a sympathetic environment and enough in the way of communication to still that impulse to work in a different way, I think that there is a fair chance that a process can be formalised in such a way where really quite different personalities can fit into it.'[129]

Grimshaw's view is that:

'There are very few people, if you have an exciting project, that you can't wind up in the end. We have started off with people we thought were very stick-in-the-mud engineers and gradually won them over and got them to be the most enthusiastic participants in every possible way and in every design meeting.'[130]

Foster and Grimshaw have therefore found it possible to form successful design teams with engineers who were not inclined to become involved in the discursive way of evolving the form of a building. Foster also points out that his involvement with Tony Hunt came about for other reasons of personal connection rather than from a belief that Hunt would necessarily be an effective collaborator in the new method of working:

'The reason that Tony was selected as an engineer was no more simple nor complex than the fact that he was the only engineer that, as a team, we had any experience with and the reason that we went to Tony was that Wendy (Foster) had worked with him on a housing scheme in Paddington. Tony was the first choice through that connection because neither Richard nor myself, any of us, had had any first-hand contact with engineers in this country. Ours was the philosophy which changed Tony Hunt's way of working because Tony Hunt had never before come in contact with any architects who sat him down at a table before they had a design.'[131]

In fact, Hunt, worked in this way with Neave Brown at Lyons, Israel and Ellis, with Tom Hancock, from the Wallingford days and with many architects during his time with Samuely, all before working with Foster and Rogers in Team 4. What is clear, however, is that there was obviously a desire on both sides to collaborate in this way and Team 4 and Hunt were able to develop this together and demonstrate its advantages.

It seems likely that the architects who were interested in evolving a new vocabulary based on the expression of structural technology and in developing structures which were aesthetically satisfying could have brought into being the design-team methodology in the absence of figures like Hunt and Rice. It was, nevertheless, a lucky coincidence that the latter were available at the time because their interest in the combination of aesthetics and the technical obviously made the whole process much more successful than it might otherwise have been. All the architects with whom Hunt has worked testify to this. Foster, for example, acknowledges that Hunt's personal qualities were important to the successful functioning of the design teams of which he was part:

'Obviously, "chemistry" is everything in terms of working relationships and somebody who is essentially sympathetic, as Tony is, as an individual with a fairly wide range of interests and an open mind is obviously more conducive to creative results, and in that sense Tony obviously has qualities which set him apart from others. I think that Tony was also part of a wider social circle where social exchanges with architects were not exceptional. It was a world that Tony moved around in. Also, I think that Tony shared a love of sketching that I have always had. I can describe my idea of hell as being without paper and pencil and I think that Tony intuitively resorts to sketching as a means of communication.'[132]

Richard Rogers also recalls attributes possessed by Hunt that made him a very effective member of a design team:

'He has an inquiring mind. He can see numerous ways of tackling a problem. He will lay them out very clearly and he can back them up with arguments. He is not a passive engineer. He belongs to the tradition of the creative architect or engineer who is reactive and they basically join from the first client meeting onwards and are part of the design team.'[133]

Grimshaw's view is:

'When you get an empathy with an engineer you do feel that it is a real conversation and certainly that was the case with Tony who likes architecture and understands the creative side of it.'[134]

He also says:

'One of Tony's strengths is that he is able to show you a number of different ways of doing it. He is also quite good at being apolitical about the architectural solution.'

Tony Hunt has been extremely effective as a member of design teams, possessing the capacity both to generate and to respond to new ideas. This requires creative imagination, on the one hand, and suppression of the ego on the other and Hunt possesses the appropriate combination of these. There is little doubt that this combination of qualities contributed significantly to the success of the early High Tech buildings because it allowed him to guide the architecture in a direction that made undesirable compromises with structure unnecessary and which resulted in buildings which performed well both technically and aesthetically. The team-based way of working which he, with others, has pioneered and which is expressed in the continuing working practices of AHA, is perhaps even more significant for the realisation of more recent highly complex building forms such as the Waterloo Terminal, the National Botanic Garden of Wales and the Eden Project. If yet further extended to include still other disciplines within the basic dialogue of the design teams, it may lead to even more exciting architectural developments.

Conclusion

Tony Hunt is an individual who expresses his wide-ranging enthusiasms in his work, and who collaborates with architects in order to create exciting new architectural forms. His preoccupations are good engineering and satisfying aesthetics. He believes that the objects which society produces should be beautiful as well as useful. He has been concerned with the making of buildings which work well and which make economic use of resources, both human and material. A congenial person who gets on with people, he was instrumental in forming the design teams and the collaborative methodologies which made possible High Tech and other later developments that successfully combine architecture and structure. The architects were obviously also important, as were other engineers such as Peter Rice and Ted Happold who had similar though different agendas. Tony Hunt's role, both personally and as part of AHA, in the continued development of the architecture of the late twentieth and early twenty-first centuries has, however, been individual, distinctive and significant.

Appendix
Key staff/ Job references

Alexandra Road
John Austin, Richard Clack

British Antarctic Survey — Halley Bay
Mark Whitby

Don Valley Stadium
Steve Morley, Martin Cranidge

IBM Cosham
Laurie Fogg

INMOS
David Hemmings, Allan Bernau, Alan Jones

Leicester Library
Leslie Stebbings, John Allen

Newport High School
Fraser Gleig, John Austin

Patera
Mark Whitby

Sainsbury Centre
John Carter

SAPA
Laurie Fogg

Schlumberger
Alan Jones

Sobell Pavilions (Ape and Monkey Houses)
Brian Foster, David Tasker

UOP Fragrancies
Brian Foster

Waterloo Terminal
Alan Jones, Mike Otiet

Willis, Faber and Dumas
Laurie Fogg, David Hemmings

Early Associates
Richard Clack, Brian Foster, Laurie Fogg,
Leslie Stebbings.

Directors and Associates

Chairman
Tony Hunt
CEng, FIStructE, DLitt, Hon FRIBA, FRSA

Managing Director
David Hemmings

Company Secretary
David Hemmings

Directors
Allan Bernau
BSc, CEng, MIStructE

Alan Jones
BSc (Hons), CEng, FIStructE

Les Postawa
IEng, AMIStructE

Björn Watson
BSc (Hons), CEng, MIStructE, MICE

Associates

Jonathan Carr
BEng (Hons), CEng, MIStructE, MPhil

David Hamilton
BSc Civil Eng, MIStructE

Martin Jones
HNC Civil Eng, IEng, AMICE, BTec Water Pollution

Tony O'Neil
BEng (Hons), StructE

Wolf Mangelsdorf
Dipl-Ing Architecture, Dipl-Ing Structural Engineering,
Postgraduate Studies in Earthquake Engineering, Kyoto

Paul Swainson
CEng, MIStructE, MICE, BSc (Hons)
1st Class StructE

Endnotes

Chapter One

1. Lambot, I, (Ed.), *Norman Foster; Buildings and Projects*, Volume 1 (1964-1973), Watermark, Hong Kong, (1991).

2. Tony Hunt, in interview with the author.

3. Kenneth Frampton and Yukio Futagawa, *Modern Architecture 1920-1945*, Rizzoli, New York, (1983), p 432.

4. Glancey, J, *New British Architecture*, Thames and Hudson, London, (1989), p 16.

5. Kidder Smith, G E, *The New Architecture of Europe*, Penguin, Harmondsworth, (1962), p 36.

6. Joedicke, J, *Architecture Since 1945*, Pall Mall Press, London, (1969), p 110.

7. *Op cit*, Glancey, J, (1989), p 21.

8. Rogers, in interview with the author.

9. 'Postmodern' and 'Postmodernism', spelt as one word, are used here to refer to a style of architecture. They should not be confused with the term post-Modern in the broad philosophical sense which refers to a complex set of ideas which form the aspects of a new 'organicist' or 'ecological' paradigm or world view, which is in the process of replacing the mechanistic paradigm of Modernism. At the beginning of the third millennium AD, the developing thinking in most fields of human activity is based on ideas which are post-Modern in this broad and generally accepted meaning of the word rather than the local meaning often used in architectural texts. Both Postmodernism and Deconstruction in the architectural stylistic sense are considered by some commentators (e.g. Ghirardo and Ibelings) to be in fact simply sub-styles of Modernism and by others (e.g. Gablik) to be part of the 'de-constructive' critique of Modernism.

10. *Op cit*, Glancey, (1989), p 8.

11. Ghirardo, D, *Architecture After Modernism*, Thames and Hudson, London, (1996), cover blurb.

12. Ghirardo (1996) *Ibid*, p 196.

13. Ghirardo (1996) *Ibid*, p 82.

14. Chief amongst these was Charles Jencks who provided a well reasoned critique of the banalities of much of the post-war Modern architecture in the early chapters of *The language of Post Modern architecture*, Academy Editions, London, (1977).

15. *Op cit*, Ghirardo, D, (1996), p 26.

16. Ghirardo (1996) *Ibid*, p 37.

17. Hans Ibelings, for example, in *Supermodernism*, NAi Publishers, Rotterdam, (1998), has this to say: ' … a lot of Postmodernist architecture is not much different from the *ersatz* architecture which came in for such a drubbing in Charles Jencks's *The Language of Post Modern Architecture* (London, (1977). What Postmodern architecture had to offer was in many cases not much more than a (sometimes) historicising décor …', p 69.

18. Gablik, S, *The Re-enchantment of Art*, Thames and Hudson, New York, (1991).

19. This term was used by Charles Jencks in an article in Jencks, C, (Ed), *New science = New architecture*, Academy Editions, London, (1997), in which he discussed the non-linear architecture of architects such as Eisenman, Gehry, Koolhaus and Miralles.

Chapter Two

20. In the late 1990s the staff complement of AHA was around 60, compared to around 5000 for Ove Arup and Partners and around 600 for Buro Happold.

21. Tony Hunt, in an unpublished account of the work of AHA.

22. Tony Hunt, following early successful collaborations with High Tech architects, was to become known as 'Meccano man'; the coining of this nickname has been attributed to Peter Cook.

23. Tony Hunt, in Lambot, I (Ed), *Norman Foster, Team 4 and Foster Associates*, Watermark, London, (1991), p 144.

24. The recollections of Foster and Rogers concerning the beginning of the working relationship between Team 4 and Hunt are different. Foster believes that it came about through a collaboration between his wife, Wendy Foster, and Tony Hunt on a housing scheme in Paddington in London on which Hunt had acted as engineer. In the Foster version, Tony Hunt was invited to become involved with Team 4 because he was the only engineer that they knew anything about. Rogers recollection was that Hunt was suggested to them by Felix Samuely, who had been Rogers' structures tutor at the Architectural Association. Neither of these accounts is incompatible with Tony Hunt's own recollection.

25. Tony Hunt, in interview with the author.

26. It had an initial contract value of £4·98 million.

27. Unpublished account by Tony Hunt of the work of AHA.

28. *Ibid*.

29   Tony Hunt, in interview with the author.

30   *Op cit*, Unpublished account by Tony Hunt of the work of AHA.

31   *Ibid*

32   Tony Hunt, in interview with the author.

33   Hunt, A, *Tony Hunt's Sketchbook,* Architectural Press, Oxford, (1999).

34   Tony Hunt, in interview with the author.

35   Tony Hunt, in interview with the author.

36   Hunt A, *Tony Hunt's Sketchbook,* Architectural Press, Oxford, (1999).

37   John Young, of the Richard Rogers partnership, in interview with the author.

38   The Paris office became independent at the time of the buyout from YRM.

Chapter Three

39   The frenetic atmosphere of the Team 4 office at this time is well described in Bryan Appleyard, *Richard Rogers, a biography,* Faber and Faber, London, (1986).

40   Rogers, in interview with the author.

41   Rogers, *The Sunday Times,* 27 Feb., 1983, quoted in Lambot (1991), p 84.

42   *Ibid.* p 76.

43   Tony Hunt, in interview with the author.

44   These internal courtyards were not realised in the finished building, however, and their omission may have contributed to one of the building's shortcomings — the uncongenial working conditions that led to the workforce negotiating special rest breaks to relieve the tedium of the working environment. It is tempting to draw attention here to the incompatibility of the aesthetic and social objectives — something that was to recur in the architecture of both Foster and Rogers. In such cases of incompatibility, the aesthetic requirement has always been given a higher priority.

45   Tony Hunt, in interview with the author.

46   Rogers, *The Sunday Times,* 27 Feb., 1983, quoted in *Op cit,* Lambot (1991), p 77.

47   The design team for Reliance Controls consisted of Norman Foster, Richard Rogers and Tony Hunt with Loren Butt, an architect then working with Richard Horden, and John Walker of the quantity surveyors, Hanscomb Partnership. The design approach was developed in a series of meetings in the Team 4 office and, in Tony Hunt's view, it is difficult now to identify who contributed any particular feature of the design. The idea of reducing the building to a minimum number of repetitive parts can be attributed to Hunt, however, who has always been passionate about discrete elements and joints.

48   Tony Hunt, in interview with the author.

49   *Ibid.*

Chapter Four

50   Amery, C, *British Architecture Today,* Electa, Milan, (1991).

51   *Ibid.*

52   Sudjic, D, *Norman Foster; Richard Rogers: James Stirling,* London, (1986), p 29.

53   This enigmatic statement was made by Foster in Lambot (1991), Volume 1, p 220. The intended possible destination was, of course, the USA.

54   Wendy Foster died in 1989.

55   Introduction to *Foster Associates,* RIBA Publications, London, (1979).

56   *Foster and Partners: Architects, Designers and Planners,* Foster and Partners, London, (1997).

57   Lambot, I, (ed.), *Norman Foster: Buildings and Projects,* (4 vols.), Watermark, Hong Kong, 1989 to 1991.

58   Foster, in *Op cit,* Lambot (1991) Volume 1, p 221.

59   Foster, *Ibid,* p 220.

60   Volume 1 was published in 1991 after Volumes 2 and 3, which came out in 1989 and which dealt with the period 1973–85. Volumes 2 and 3 were therefore concerned with Foster Associates' most prestigious projects to 1989, such as the Willis, Faber and Dumas building, the Sainsbury Centre and the Renault Distribution Centre. Volume 1 dealt with the period up to 1973.

61   *Op cit,* Lambot (1991), Volume 1, prelim., p 4.

62   Tony Hunt, in interview with the author.

63   The wining entry of this competition, by Evans and Shalev, which was actually built, was also engineered by Hunt.

64   *Op cit,* Lambot (1991), Volume 1, p 40.

65   For example, in *Op cit,* Lambot (1991), Volume 1, p 136.

66   Tony Hunt, in interview with the author.

67   Tony Hunt, in interview with the author.

Endnotes

68 Tony Hunt, in interview with the author.

69 Tony Hunt, in interview with the author.

70 Sir Robert Sainsbury, quoted in *Op cit*, Lambot (1989), Vol. 2, p 80.

71 Foster announced this to Hunt at the start of one of the regular Thursday meetings of the design team. Hunt was reluctant at first, due to the amount of design effort that had been expended on the development of the solid-web version, but quickly appreciated the architectural virtues of a triangulated structure.

72 The most efficient cross-sectional shape for the building, from a structural viewpoint, would have been that of a catenary arch. The rectilinear cross-section of the Sainsbury Centre was significantly different from this and the structure therefore had to resist high levels of internal force. See Macdonald, A J, *Structure and Architecture*, (2000, 2nd edn) Chapter 4 for a discussion of these issues.

73 Tony Hunt, in interview with the author.

74 Tony Hunt, in private communication with the author.

75 Sutherland Lyle, *Architects' Journal*, Vol. 161, No. 23, 4 June, (1975), p 1160.

76 Dan Cruickshank, *RIBA Journal*, Vol. 104, no. 7 July 1997, p 45.

77 Kenneth Knight, company secretary of the Willis Faber Group. The quotation is from Knight's contribution to Volume 2 of the Lambot series.

78 *Op cit*, Lambot (1989), Vol. 2. See also Gabriele Bramante, *Willis, Faber and Dumas Building*, Phaidon, London, (1993).

79 Ibid, Lambot (1989), Vol. 2, p 20.

80 The earliest designs were based on a steel framework and this was the material preferred by Foster. The bad experience with 'wet' materials in the early Team 4 projects were still fresh in the memory. The use of steel would, however, have severely compromised the design. The curvilinear form and tapered, cantilevered edges of the floor slabs, which were such an essential part of the final concept, would have been virtually impossible to realise in steel with any degree of design elegance.

81 This was to be of great benefit in the construction of the WFD building, which was carried out in 1973 during the period of three-day week working that was associated with the national strike of coal miners. The very simple form of the structure allowed it to be completed in nine months, much of which was of three-day working.

Chapter Five

82 Leon Battista Alberti, *On the Art of Building in Ten Books*, (1486), tr. Rykwert, Leach and Tavernor, MIT Press, London, (1988), p 156.

83 This is an idea of beauty that acknowledges 'Nature' as the ultimate source of legitimacy and there is therefore some irony in the fact that it can be applied to many of Foster's buildings which are intended to evoke the world of technology and the machine. Foster's idea of 'perfection' has more in common with the inorganic crystal, however, than Alberti's humanist version.

84 Rogers, in interview with the author.

85 See Bryan Appleyard, *Richard Rogers, a biography,* Faber and Faber, London, (1986), p 131.

86 Foster's education at Manchester University had been more conventional and was based on the Bauhaus method with its insistence on the proper appreciation of the properties of materials and the means by which these are fashioned into useful objects and, in architectural project work, the insistence that buildings be fully described in plan, section and elevation.

87 *Op cit*, Appleyard (1986), p 65.

88 Quoted in *Op cit*, Appleyard (1986), p 138.

89 The background to Rogers' rebelliousness and iconoclasm is well articulated in Appleyard's book.

90 In retrospect it can be observed that this was something of a cry in the wilderness because the ideas which Rogers challenged continued to dominate most British architecture schools throughout the second half of the twentieth century.

91 Richard Rogers, *Architecture: a modern view,* Thames and Hudson, London, (1990).

92 Richard Rogers, in *Cities for a Small Planet,* (Philip Gumuchdjian, ed.), Faber and Faber, London, (1997).

93 The history of the steel-framed house is comprehensively reviewed in Neil Jackson, *The Modern Steel House*, Spon, London, (1996).

94 Interview with Neil Jackson. Quoted in Neil Jackson, *The Modern Steel House*, Spon, London, (1996).